A NOTE TO THE TEACHER

This book is one of a series of three course books for years 7, 8 and 9 of Keystage 3 and has the following features...

- It exactly matches both the content and the spirit of the exemplar scheme of work for Year 9 produced by the Qualifications and Curriculum Authority.

- It consists of 12 units in Year 9, each of which is 7 pages long.

- The first 4 pages consist of content and ensure complete coverage of the revised Programme of Study. The main keywords are highlighted throughout the text.

- Page 5 consists of a 'keywords' exercise and a 'comprehension' based largely on the nature, history and understanding of scientific ideas.

- Page 6 tests understanding through a literacy exercise and then goes on to develop skills involving the production or interpretation of graphs or data.

- Page 7 is devoted entirely to an investigation related to the particular unit. This can be done instead of actually doing the investigation or may be used alongside it in order to develop the investigative skills appropriate to a Year 9 pupil.

- The work is graded to provide access at level 5 as well as sufficient rigour for level 7 and above. Worksheets at 'Higher' and 'Foundation' level are available for each page of content on our website at www.lonsdalesrg.co.uk to enable further differentiation. In total there are over 300 Key Stage 3 worksheets on this site.

- Wherever possible, due consideration has been given to Language for Learning, Numeracy, ICT, PSHE, Citizenship and Key Skills.

- These course books can stand alone or may be used in conjunction with the QCA Teachers' Guide and exemplar scheme of work. However it should be noted that the exemplar scheme of work lays greatest emphasis on word and symbol equations in the four 'Materials and their properties' units. In an attempt to make this more accessible, and as a grounding for Year 10, we have included in addition to word and symbol equations, simple models to show how atoms rearrange themselves during chemical reactions.

- Remember that several topics in the QCA scheme of work will not be tested in the Year 9 National Curriculum tests. For final revision use our Key Stage 3 Revision Guide, 'The Essentials of Science - Key Stage Three' which pulls together all the material for Years 7, 8 and 9 which will be tested.

A NOTE TO THE PUPIL

We're sure that you will enjoy using this course book, but to make the most of it ...

- Tackle the questions seriously and do them to the best of your ability.

- Try to write your answers in good English using correct punctuation and good sentence construction. Read your answers back to yourself.

- Think carefully about graphical work. Make sure your axes are accurately labelled and your points constructed properly.

- Try to learn (by heart if necessary) what all the keywords mean.

Good luck

Katie Whelan

WHAT VARIATION IS

Animals of different SPECIES have obvious differences, but animals of the SAME SPECIES have less obvious differences. This is VARIATION.

This is due to different animals having different GENETIC INFORMATION in their cells ...

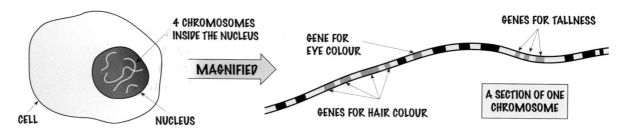

CELL   NUCLEUS   4 CHROMOSOMES INSIDE THE NUCLEUS   MAGNIFIED   GENE FOR EYE COLOUR   GENES FOR HAIR COLOUR   GENES FOR TALLNESS   A SECTION OF ONE CHROMOSOME

The nucleus of each cell contains thousands of GENES. These are arranged on CHROMOSOMES, rather like beads on a necklace. These genes are instructions which control the characteristics which develop in different individuals. It follows therefore that individuals of the same species have a lot more genes in common than individuals of different species! Even so, there is still quite a lot of variation between members of the same species. If you look at specimens of the same variety of crop eg. tomatoes or potatoes you will find differences in colour, mass, length, diameter and possibly even taste.

THE EFFECT OF ENVIRONMENTAL DIFFERENCES

Identical twins have exactly the same GENETIC INFORMATION because they were formed from the same egg and sperm. Nevertheless there can be very obvious differences between them due to their environment and way of living. Environment has a more obvious effect on plants. Differences in light, temperature, nutrients and soil acidity or alkalinity can cause huge differences.

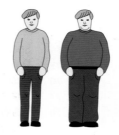 

Variation can be caused by INHERITED FACTORS, ENVIRONMENTAL FACTORS or a COMBINATION OF BOTH. Some of the characteristics which fall into these categories are shown in the pie chart opposite.

INHERITANCE
• Eye Colour
• Hair Colour
• Attached Ear Lobes
• Blood Group
• Sex
• Fingerprints

ENVIRONMENT
• Strength
• Weight
• Ability To Speak English

• Height
• Personality
• Intelligence
• Speed

• Skin Colour
• Stamina
• Fitness

INHERITANCE AND ENVIRONMENT

SEXUAL REPRODUCTION

Sexual reproduction NEEDS TWO ORGANISMS OF THE SAME SPECIES. Each of these organisms must produce specialised cells called GAMETES. In animals these are the EGG and the SPERM cells, ...
... in plants they are the EGG and the POLLEN GRAIN.
Each of these contains genetic information in the form of GENES, from either the male or female parent, which fuse together at FERTILISATION to produce a cell which will become a new individual, with features inherited from both parents.

FERTILISATION IN ANIMALS AND PLANTS

Male and female gametes fuse at fertilisation ...

... to produce a cell which contains genetic information from both parents.

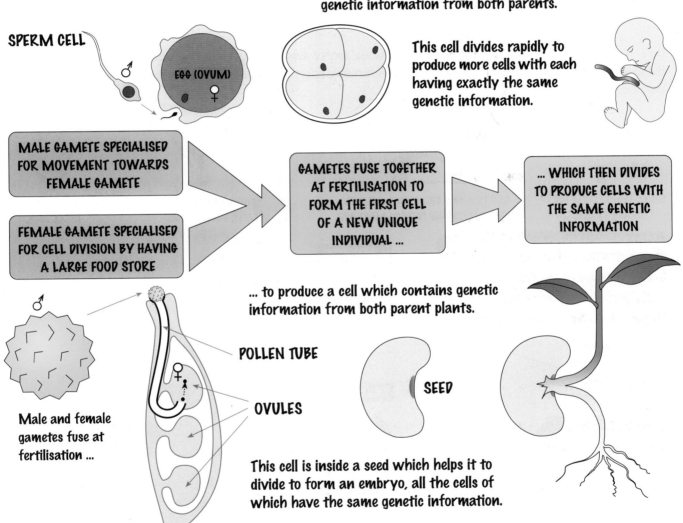

SPERM CELL

EGG (OVUM) ♂ ♀

This cell divides rapidly to produce more cells with each having exactly the same genetic information.

MALE GAMETE SPECIALISED FOR MOVEMENT TOWARDS FEMALE GAMETE

FEMALE GAMETE SPECIALISED FOR CELL DIVISION BY HAVING A LARGE FOOD STORE

GAMETES FUSE TOGETHER AT FERTILISATION TO FORM THE FIRST CELL OF A NEW UNIQUE INDIVIDUAL ...

... WHICH THEN DIVIDES TO PRODUCE CELLS WITH THE SAME GENETIC INFORMATION

... to produce a cell which contains genetic information from both parent plants.

POLLEN TUBE

OVULES

SEED

Male and female gametes fuse at fertilisation ...

This cell is inside a seed which helps it to divide to form an embryo, all the cells of which have the same genetic information.

The joining together of cells containing genetic information from the parents results in an individual which is similar to both parents, but shows quite a lot of differences to them.

ARTIFICIAL POLLINATION BY PLANT BREEDERS

When a breeder is trying to produce a new variety of plant, it is essential that the only pollen which is allowed to pollinate a chosen plant is the pollen which the breeder has selected. This often means hand-pollinating individual plants, then placing transparent plastic bags over the female reproductive organs.
(see next page for SELECTIVE BREEDING)

THE IDEA BEHIND SELECTIVE BREEDING

NEW VARIETIES of organisms can be bred by taking advantage of VARIATION.
- Organisms with a desired characteristic, are bred with similar organisms ...
- ... resulting in offspring, some of which will have an EXAGGERATED VERSION OF THIS CHARACTERISTIC.
- These are then bred again, and so on, until the desired result is achieved.

SELECTIVE BREEDING IN ANIMALS

Here, 'black patches' has been selected in order to produce 'spotty dogs' (dalmations). This is done for decorative purposes, but illustrates how new 'varieties' can be produced. In farming, selective breeding is done to improve the stock and to develop new varieties of produce.

SHORT-LEGGED SHEEP FOR UPLAND FARMS.

CATTLE WHICH GROW TO MATURITY MORE QUICKLY AND PRODUCE MORE BEEF.

COWS WHICH GIVE GREATER YIELDS OF MILK.

HENS WHICH LAY MORE EGGS.

SELECTIVE BREEDING IN PLANTS

EXAMPLES OF GREEN VEGETABLES BRED FROM A COMMON ANCESTOR

ANCESTOR

CABBAGE — Selected because of large bud

CAULIFLOWER — Selected because of large flower head

BRUSSEL SPROUTS — Selected for many small side buds

Seedless Orange

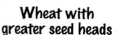

Wheat with greater seed heads

Many of our well-known fruit and vegetables would be strange looking things to someone who lived three hundred years ago, because they have been bred selectively to produce organisms which we as consumers prefer.

REMEMBER THOUGH! ... IT TAKES MANY GENERATIONS TO GET THE DESIRED RESULT.

DANGERS OF SELECTIVE BREEDING

Too much selective breeding can cause individual genes to be lost from the breeding population. This loss of a particular characteristic is something to avoid, because once it's gone, it's gone forever - ie. there is a loss of variation in the population. To prevent this, RARE BREED SANCTUARIES look after breeds which are no longer used on farms so that useful genes are not lost forever.

ASEXUAL REPRODUCTION

Asexual reproduction only NEEDS ONE ORGANISM. This can produce other organisms without the need for genetic material from another individual.

- A simple single-celled animal like an AMOEBA can divide to produce new GENETICALLY-IDENTICAL offspring ...

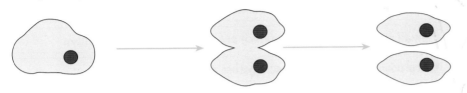

Both these new amoebae have exactly the same genes as their parent.

- Plants can also produce genetically-identical offspring ... eg. the spider plant.

CLONING

CLONES are genetically identical individuals. Identical twins are clones of each other, formed when an EMBRYO splits into two. This is a relatively rare but completely natural event.

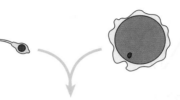

FERTILISATION, then CELL DIVISION, followed by ...

... splitting of the embryo into TWO which are GENETICALLY IDENTICAL.

ARTIFICIAL CLONING

Here, steps are taken to ensure that all the genetic material comes from one parent. In gardening, a simple method is to take CUTTINGS of a plant that you'd like to have lots of ...

With animals the procedure is much more difficult ...

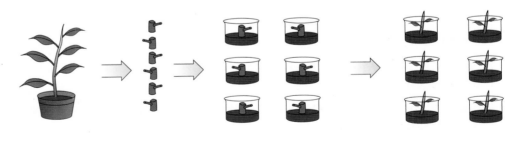

PRIZE EWE

An egg cell is stimulated to behave as though it has been fertilised. It divides several times to form a ball of cells which is ...

... then split apart into several clumps, before the cells become specialised.

These embryos are then implanted into the uteruses of sheep who will eventually give birth to clones.

KEYWORDS

Match the keywords from this unit to their definitions ...

Keyword	Definition
VARIATION	Units which determine an individual's characteristics
SPECIES	Using variation to produce a desired characteristic
GENES	Small sections from a plant which are grown in different locations
CHROMOSOMES	Reproductive cells which fuse together at fertilisation
SEXUAL REPRODUCTION	Differences within the same species
GAMETES	Fertilisation in plants caused by human interaction
FERTILISATION	A particular type of plant or animal
ARTIFICIAL POLLINATION	Producing exact copies of a plant or animal
VARIETIES	Structure which carries lots of different genes arranged like beads on a necklace
SELECTIVE BREEDING	Production of offspring requiring two parents
CLONING	Producing offspring without interaction with other organisms
EMBRYO	The range of different types within a species
CUTTINGS	The fusing of male and female gametes
ASEXUAL REPRODUCTION	An animal or plant in its early stages of development

IMPROVING THE FOOD WE EAT

Read this passage and then answer the questions below.

Many of the food products we take for granted today would have been unrecognisable to someone who lived 300 years ago because they have been bred selectively for characteristics which are desirable. All our fruit and vegetables are bigger, more disease resistant, and have a longer shelf-life. Our sheep and cattle produce more milk, more meat, more wool and come to maturity faster. 'Breeding the best with the best and hoping for the best' was the principle behind selective breeding, but with the development of cloning the effect of chance can be removed. If you can produce the ideal variety of organism why let sexual reproduction introduce variation into its offspring when the organism can simply be cloned, producing 100% genetically identical offspring? This has been done for many years by horticulturists who simply propagate new varieties of plants by taking cuttings. The cloning of animals however has proved more difficult and the technique still requires more research before it can be viewed as an acceptable practice.

1. Do you think it is likely that <u>all</u> food products are better today then they ever have been, in every respect?

2. Describe one serious problem caused by too much selective breeding.

3. Explain what you think is meant by, 'breeding the best with the best and hoping for the best'?

4. How does sexual reproduction increase variation?

5. Is the cloning of plants more acceptable than the cloning of animals? Explain the reasons for your answer.

SEXUAL AND ASEXUAL REPRODUCTION

Sexual reproduction depends on the fusion of two .... which are cells specialised for this job. In humans

they are the .... and the .... , one of which is specialised for .... and the

other by having a large .... The moment of fusion is called .... when

the .... from the two cells is combined to form a genetically ....

individual. This new individual now carries .... from both its .... and as a result may have

similar .... to one or other of them.

Asexual reproduction doesn't depend on .... at all since only one .... is involved.

Plants are far .... at this method of reproduction since only relatively .... animals,

such as amoeba, are capable of it.

The offspring produced by this method are .... and show no ....

Because of this, gardeners often produce more plants by taking .... , since they know the offspring

will be exactly like the parents.

SELECTIVE BREEDING IN RACEHORSES

The following data shows how the average time taken for a racehorse to run one mile has changed over the last
200 years. Plot this data onto the graph paper provided and then answer the questions below.

YEARS	1800	1830	1850	1860	1880	1900	1920	1930	1950	1960	1980	1990	2000
TIME (s)	105	100.5	98.5	97.5	96.0	94.5	93.5	93.0	92.5	92.0	91.5	91.5	91.5

1. What would the average speed have been in 1820?

....

2. In which year would the average time taken
   have been 99.5 secs?

....

3. Describe how this data may have been obtained.

....

....

....

4. Describe what you would expect to happen over the next two hundred years, and explain your predictions.

....

....

....

Some year 9 students were investigating whether a particular variety of potato was affected by the method of reproduction used to produce it. Their teacher grew some potatoes from seeds formed as a result of cross pollinating two plants. He also allowed one of the two plants to reproduce asexually. All the potatoes produced were washed and weighed. The following results were obtained for the two groups of potato.

Group 1: (Mass in g.) 106, 108, 107, 105, 110, 103, 109, 107, 105, 104, 110, 109, 102, 101, 103, 102, 104, 107, 106, 106, 109, 110, 102, 105, 106, 107, 108, 101, 100, 107, 106, 105, 102, 108, 106, 105, 103, 102.

Group 2: (Mass in g.) 93, 97, 98, 101, 106, 111, 117, 119, 103, 115, 97, 106, 105, 107, 112, 92, 102, 108, 104, 106, 103, 96, 101, 109, 104, 94, 111, 97, 110, 102, 113, 114, 99, 110.

Group 1

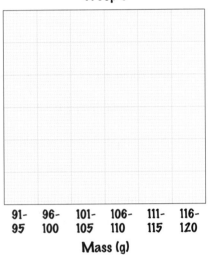

| 91-95 | 96-100 | 101-105 | 106-110 | 111-115 | 116-120 |

Mass (g)

Group 2

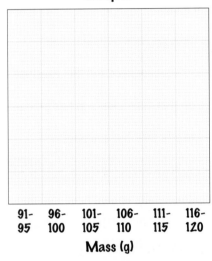

| 91-95 | 96-100 | 101-105 | 106-110 | 111-115 | 116-120 |

Mass (g)

1. Tally the results and plot them as bar charts onto the graph paper above. You must be careful to choose an appropriate scale for the vertical axis.

2. Explain which of the two groups has been produced through sexual reproduction.

....

....

3. What precautions would the teacher have had to take when cross-pollinating the two plants?

....

....

4. What other factors would have to be controlled in order to make this a fair test?

....

....

....

5. Describe briefly one improvement you would make to this investigation.

....

....

THE RESPIRATORY AND THE DIGESTIVE SYSTEMS

- The respiratory system takes OXYGEN from the atmosphere into the blood and at the same time removes carbon dioxide. The lungs are the main organ of the respiratory system and they are specially adapted to provide a large surface area for gas exchange.

- The digestive system breaks down large insoluble food molecules into small soluble ones such as GLUCOSE. We use glucose for energy but we need many other things if we want to have a BALANCED DIET.

THE CIRCULATORY SYSTEM

- The heart, blood vessels and blood transport GLUCOSE and OXYGEN (and other things) around the body. To do this well, the system has to remain in good condition.

- The heart is a working muscle and so needs exercise to stay in good shape. Exercise also helps to improve the blood flow through the blood vessels.

- A bad diet (particularly too much fat), smoking, too much alcohol and lack of exercise can cause the blood vessels to 'fur up' (ARTERIOSCLEROSIS). This can lead to poor circulation, heart attacks and general loss of efficiency because oxygen and food aren't transported to the cells as well as they should be.

THE SKELETAL AND MUSCLE SYSTEMS

- Glucose and oxygen are used in all cells to release energy in the process of RESPIRATION. The most obvious example of this, however, would be in muscle cells where the energy released in respiration is transferred into MOVEMENT energy.

- Muscles work by shortening, and use the long bones of the body as levers. This produces a wide range of movement.

- Exercising the muscles is a good thing for general fitness, but remember that there are different ways of being fit. A person should try to achieve some degree of STRENGTH, SUPPLENESS, SPEED, STAMINA and good body SHAPE.

- The skeleton, you will remember, supports and protects our body besides providing a framework for movement.

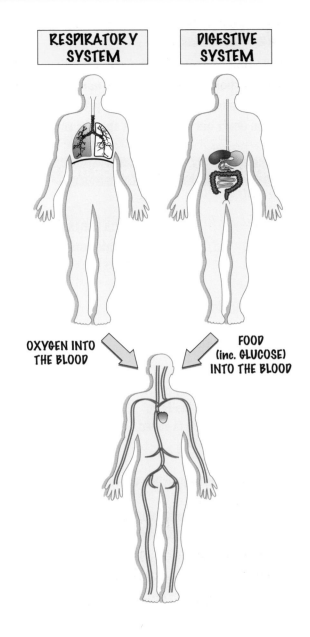

RESPIRATORY SYSTEM   DIGESTIVE SYSTEM

OXYGEN INTO THE BLOOD

FOOD (inc. GLUCOSE) INTO THE BLOOD

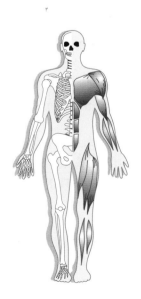

A BALANCED DIET

You will remember from year eight that a balanced diet contains proteins, fats, carbohydrates, vitamins, minerals, fibre and water. The three main items are usually needed in the proportions shown in the pie chart alongside. If you don't get enough of a specific nutrient, it can lead to a specific disease.

FAT 25-30%
CARBOHYDRATE 55-60%
PROTEIN 15-20%

PROBLEMS CAUSED BY POOR DIET

Not enough VITAMIN A leads to poor night vision.

Lack of CALCIUM causes weak bones and teeth.

Lack of VITAMIN C leads to bleeding gums and joints. This is called scurvy.

Too little PROTEIN causes wasting of body tissues.

Not enough IRON causes anaemia which makes you feel weary.

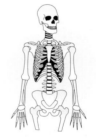

Absence of VITAMIN D leads to soft bones. This is called RICKETS.

Too much food, particularly fat, results in OBESITY and heart disease.

Good health is impossible without a good diet and this is one of the reasons that people live much longer nowadays.

HEALTHY MUSCLES AND JOINTS

- The skeleton provides SUPPORT and PROTECTION, but also provides a FRAMEWORK OF LEVERS FOR MUSCLE ATTACHMENT. These levers are, of course, bones which are connected to each other at joints.

- Muscles can only CONTRACT (shorten) and so can only pull bones.
- Because of this they act in ANTAGONISTIC PAIRS to oppose each other's movement.
- Muscles are attached to bones by NON-ELASTIC TENDONS.
- To bend the arm muscle B contracts and muscle A relaxes, and vice versa to straighten it.

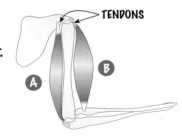

TENDONS

A   B

- Bones are attached to other bones by SLIGHTLY ELASTIC LIGAMENTS.
- A layer of CARTILAGE prevents wear of the surfaces in contact.
- A small amount of FLUID also helps to reduce friction.

There are several types of joint, the most important of which are ...

1. HINGE JOINTS	Knee joint, Elbow joint.
2. BALL and SOCKET JOINTS	Shoulder joint, Hip joint.
3. PARTLY MOVABLE JOINTS	Joints between Ribs and Breast Bone.
4. FIXED JOINTS	Joints between the Skull bones.

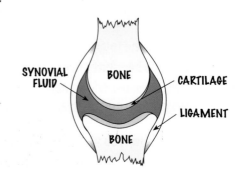

SYNOVIAL FLUID
BONE
CARTILAGE
LIGAMENT
BONE

THE REASON FOR BREATHING

In RESPIRATION cells release energy from glucose by combining it with OXYGEN. This oxygen is carried to cells by the bloodstream ... ... which picks it up in the LUNGS.

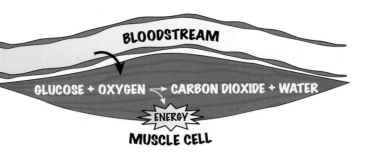

BLOODSTREAM

GLUCOSE + OXYGEN → CARBON DIOXIDE + WATER

ENERGY

MUSCLE CELL

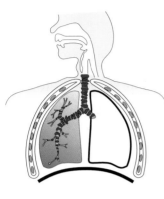

Breathing constantly 'freshens up' the air inside your lungs, replacing the oxygen which has been taken up by the blood. The chest wall is raised and lowered by the rib muscles so that it acts like bellows drawing air into and out of the lungs.

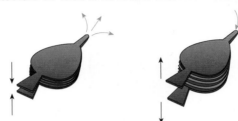

CLEANING UP THE AIR

Specialised cells line all of the respiratory system. Some produce MUCUS, while others have hairs called CILIA which beat the mucus upwards to the mouth. This mucus traps dust and microbes which get pushed out of the lungs and are eventually swallowed. Sometimes when you have a cold you produce too much mucus and have to cough to 'clear your chest'.

ONE OF THE BREATHING TUBES

MUCUS

GLAND CELLS

CILIATED EPITHELIAL CELLS

THE EFFECTS OF SMOKING

If the ingredients of cigarette smoke are 'sucked' through cotton wool you will see a brown tarry deposit build up. This smells awful and has a shocking effect on the human body ...

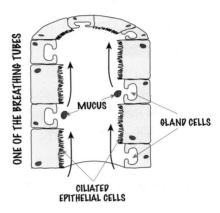

The cilia stop 'beating' because of the tar, causing mucus to build up.

Constant coughing due to build up of mucus damages the air sacs. This is called EMPHYSEMA.

The tar also causes cancer of the lungs, throat, mouth and stomach.

NICOTINE is addictive and narrows blood vessels, increases heart rate and therefore increases blood pressure.

BRONCHITIS caused by smoke particles and increased mucus.

Carbon monoxide in the cigarette smoke gets picked up by the blood more easily than oxygen.

Arterial disease leads to heart attacks, strokes and even amputations.

Increased risk of chest infections.

ALCOHOL

In moderation this is relatively harmless. However alcohol abuse and dependency can cause serious problems ...

- ### LIVER DAMAGE

  Alcohol is a mild poison and causes parts of the liver to become fibrous and therefore useless.

- ### IMPAIRED JUDGEMENT

  This is while under the influence of alcohol. Acts of bravado or foolhardiness can have fatal effects.

- ### BRAIN DAMAGE

  Regular doses lead to increased brain cell death and a drop in mental performance eg. memory.

- ### ADDICTION

  Extreme alcohol dependency can lead to regular days off, reduced performance at work, violence and money problems.

SOLVENTS

The vapour from various household substances is inhaled. Examples include glues and paints. This practice can cause the following problems ...

- ### HALLUCINATIONS

  Users may lose their grip on reality.

- ### PERSONALITY CHANGE

  Users may start to display different personality traits.

- ### DAMAGE TO ORGANS

  Including lungs, brain, liver and kidneys. This is usually permanent.

OTHER DRUGS

- ### HALLUCINOGENS

  eg. Ecstasy, L.S.D. These cause hallucinations, and in the case of Ecstasy the feeling of being full of energy, which can lead to dehydration and collapse.

- ### DEPRESSANTS

  eg. Alcohol (see above), Barbiturates, depress the nervous system.

- ### STIMULANTS

  eg. Amphetamine ('speed'), Methedrine. Users become psychologically dependent on the feelings of energy they can cause. Can cause change in personality.

- ### PAIN KILLERS

  eg. Heroin, Morphine. Addiction and complete collapse of personality and self-discipline.

KEYWORDS

Match the keywords from this unit to their definitions ...

GLUCOSE	Sticky liquid which traps dust and microbes in the respiratory system
ARTERIOSCLEROSIS	Muscles which act in opposite directions around a joint
RESPIRATION	A smoking related disease caused by excessive mucus and smoke particles
ANTAGONISTIC PAIRS	Small soluble molecule used for energy
TENDONS	Tiny hairs which move mucus along the respiratory tract
LIGAMENTS	An addictive substance found in cigarettes
CARTILAGE	'Furring up' of the blood vessels
CILIA	This prevents the wear of surfaces in contact inside joints
MUCUS	They give feelings of energy
EMPHYSEMA	They attach one bone to another
NICOTINE	Substances which cause hallucinations
BRONCHITIS	They attach the muscles to the bones
HALLUCINOGENS	The release of energy from glucose inside cells
STIMULANTS	Condition in which air sacs are damaged due to constant coughing

INVESTIGATING THE CAUSES OF LUNG CANCER

Read this passage and then answer the questions below.

Scientists investigating the increase in deaths from lung cancer during the 1940's and 1950's began to suspect that the underlying cause was related to smoking. At the time many people assumed that smoking was safe and thought that it was rather sophisticated - an impression that was reinforced through heavy advertising by the tobacco companies.

A major study compared a group of smokers and a group of non-smokers over a long period of time. The study showed that the smokers were more likely to get lung cancer than non-smokers, and that the more a person smoked, the greater were their chances of getting lung cancer.

The non-smokers in this study were called the 'control group' and were chosen so as to differ from the smoking group only in the fact that they had never smoked. The results of the study provoked a hostile reaction from the tobacco companies and came as a shock to many people. However it took many years to build up public awareness of the dangers of smoking, partly due to the cigarette manufacturers huge advertising budgets.

1. How might advertising be used to create the impression that smoking is 'cool'?

2. Describe several ways in which the 'smoking group' and the 'control group' should be identical in order to make this a fair test.

3. Why do you think that the results of the study should have provoked a hostile reaction from the tobacco companies?

4. Comment on the following statement, 'being a smoker means that you will definitely get lung cancer at some stage.'

5. Comment on the following statement, 'I can't possibly get lung cancer smoking just 5 cigarettes a day.'

DRINKING AND DRUGS

.... abuse is a common problem though sadly many people are unaware that alcohol is a mild

.... , which can cause both long- and short-term problems. When under the influence of alcohol your

risk of injury and accidents is .... as your judgement is severely .... - this can be fatal.

On a more long-term outlook, if someone becomes dependent on alcohol and develops an .... they may

begin to take days off work, and performance, violence and money can be a problem. Quite often, parts of their

liver will become .... and useless and their .... cells will deteriorate more quickly, causing a

drop in .... performance eg. memory. Alcohol is only one of the many .... frequently used

today. There has also been an increase in the use of .... such as Ecstasy and .... and

.... such as .... ('speed'). Solvent abuse, where the vapour of household substances is

.... , can cause hallucinations, ... and permanent damage to .... ,

such as the .... , brain and ....

SMOKING AND LUNG CANCER

Plot the following two sets of data onto the graph paper provided.

NUMBER OF CIGARETTES SMOKED PER DAY	10	20	30	40	50
INCREASED RISK OF DYING OF LUNG CANCER	x10	x18	x25	x33	x40

YEAR	1920	1930	1940	1950	1960
NUMBER OF DEATHS PER 100,000 DUE TO LUNG CANCER	10	35	50	100	180

1. What conclusions can be drawn from the first set of results?

....

....

2. What conclusions can be drawn from the second set of results?

....

....

In an investigation into heart rate a group of pupils decided to exercise for **5 minutes** and then take their pulse rates at **30 second intervals**. They exercised at the same time by stepping on and off some classroom chairs and produced the following data by taking their pulse for **15 seconds at 30 second intervals**.

NAME	IMMEDIATELY AFTER EXERCISE	AFTER 30 SECONDS	AFTER 60 SECONDS	AFTER 90 SECONDS	AFTER 120 SECONDS	AFTER 150 SECONDS	AFTER 180 SECONDS
GRACE	37	34	32	29	26	23	20
YASMIN	37	32	29	27	25	23	21
JAMES	37	26	21	19	18	18	18
OLIVIA	36	31	27	24	22	20	18
ZACH	35	28	24	22	20	19	18

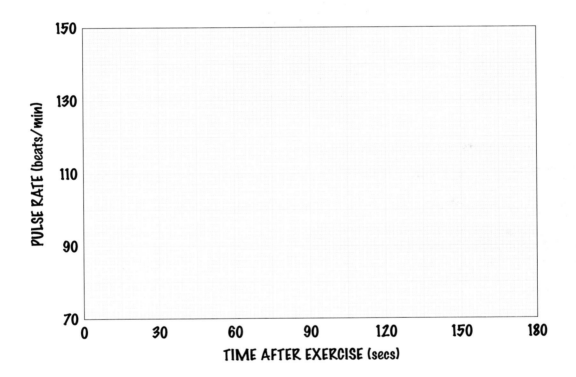

1. Plot these results onto the graph paper using different coloured pencils.

2. What variables should be controlled in order to make this a fair test?

....

....

3. Whose pulse rate returns to 'normal' fastest?

....

4. Why does pulse rate increase during exercise?

....

5. How might this method of recording pulse rate be improved?

....

MAKING FOOD FROM SUNLIGHT

Green plants <u>don't</u> absorb food from the soil. They make their own using sunlight. This is called PHOTOSYNTHESIS, which actually means 'making through light', and it occurs in the cells of green plants, which are exposed to light ...

<u>4 things are needed ...</u>

LIGHT from the sun

CARBON DIOXIDE from the air

WATER from the soil

CHLOROPHYLL in the leaves

... and 2 things are produced

GLUCOSE increases the biomass of a plant and provides energy

OXYGEN released to the atmosphere

THE WORD EQUATION FOR PHOTOSYNTHESIS

$$\text{CARBON DIOXIDE} + \text{WATER} \xrightarrow[\text{CHLOROPHYLL}]{\text{LIGHT}} \text{GLUCOSE} + \text{OXYGEN}$$

THE SYMBOL EQUATION FOR PHOTOSYNTHESIS

$$6CO_2 + 6H_2O \longrightarrow C_6H_{12}O_6 + 6O_2$$

$$6 \times \quad + \quad 6 \times \quad \longrightarrow \quad \quad + \quad 6 \times$$

Of course you don't need to know the structure of a glucose molecule but it's interesting to see how the CO_2 and H_2O molecules are rearranged to form it.

THE PRODUCTS OF PHOTOSYNTHESIS

1. **OXYGEN** passes out of the cells in which it is made and then out of the leaves into the atmosphere.

2. **GLUCOSE** from photosynthesis is used in many different ways.
   a) ... to produce energy via respiration for all living processes in the plant.
   b) ... to produce protein for new growth **[BIOMASS]**.
   c) ... to make **CELLULOSE** for new cell walls.
   d) ... to make oils for storage in seeds.
   e) ... to make **STARCH** for storage in stems and underground tubers.

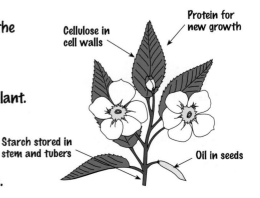

Cellulose in cell walls

Protein for new growth

Starch stored in stem and tubers

Oil in seeds

LEAVES - THE FOOD FACTORIES

The leaves provide an enormous surface area with which to photosynthesise. They even 'fan out' so that they don't shade each other. The main area for PHOTOSYNTHESIS, however, contains cells which are specially ADAPTED for this purpose on the upper surface of the leaf ...

... they are LONG, THIN and PACKED WITH CHLOROPLASTS which contain the green pigment CHLOROPHYLL, which is essential

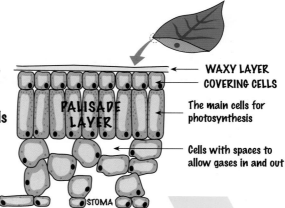

WAXY LAYER COVERING CELLS

The main cells for photosynthesis

Cells with spaces to allow gases in and out

PALISADE LAYER

STOMA

for photosynthesis. The shape of the cells means that nearly all the light falling on the leaf is absorbed by the chloroplasts in these cells.

TESTING LEAVES FOR STARCH

The glucose formed by photosynthesising leaves is usually converted to starch for storage, and we can test for starch in leaves by using IODINE. IODINE is a pale brown colour which turns BLUE-BLACK on contact with starch.

IODINE

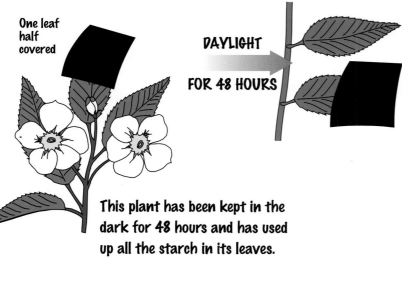

One leaf half covered

DAYLIGHT

FOR 48 HOURS

This plant has been kept in the dark for 48 hours and has used up all the starch in its leaves.

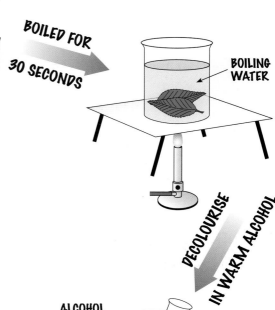

BOILED FOR

30 SECONDS

BOILING WATER

DECOLOURISE IN WARM ALCOHOL

ALCOHOL

HOT WATER

TURN OFF BUNSEN!

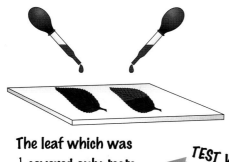

HOT WATER

DIP IN WATER TO SOFTEN

TEST WITH IODINE

The leaf which was $\frac{1}{2}$ covered only tests positive for starch in the uncovered bit.

THE STRUCTURE OF ROOTS

Roots form a massive branching structure under the ground. Just like the trunk of a tree, they start off thick and divide into smaller and smaller branches. The finest of these branches give the root a fibrous structure which provides a massive surface area.

Inside the roots is a system of tubes which run upwards into the stem and eventually into the leaves. These transport water and minerals to all parts of the plant. They are grouped in bundles called **VASCULAR BUNDLES.**

ROOT HAIR CELLS

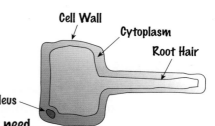

Cell Wall
Cytoplasm
Root Hair
Nucleus

These specialised cells are specially adapted to provide an even bigger surface area. They are found on the outside of the finest rootlets and have a 'hair-like' projection sticking out of them. This is where water and minerals are absorbed by the plant. Because these are living cells, they need OXYGEN for RESPIRATION and so there has to be oxygen available in the soil. If plants get waterlogged due to flooding, the stagnant water often contains little or no oxygen and so even though there's lots of water and minerals, the root hair cells die and the plant can't absorb water or minerals and so also dies.

HOW THE PLANT USES THE WATER IT ABSORBS

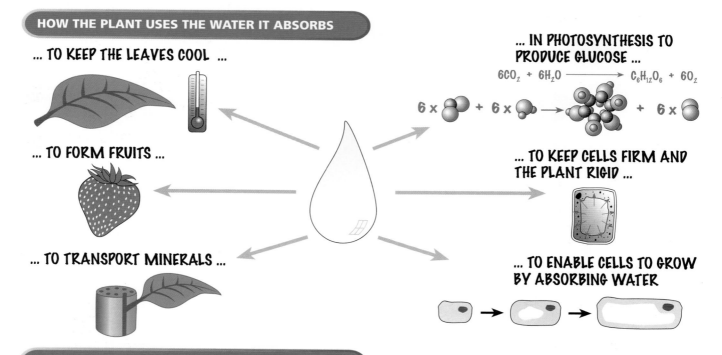

... TO KEEP THE LEAVES COOL ...

... IN PHOTOSYNTHESIS TO PRODUCE GLUCOSE ...

$$6CO_2 + 6H_2O \longrightarrow C_6H_{12}O_6 + 6O_2$$

$6 \times$ + $6 \times$ → + $6 \times$

... TO FORM FRUITS ...

... TO KEEP CELLS FIRM AND THE PLANT RIGID ...

... TO TRANSPORT MINERALS ...

... TO ENABLE CELLS TO GROW BY ABSORBING WATER

HOW THE PLANT USES THE MINERALS IT ABSORBS

Besides the CARBON, HYDROGEN and OXYGEN present in glucose, plants need other elements in order to grow successfully and be healthy. They need ...

NITROGEN (in the form of nitrates) to produce PROTEIN	POTASSIUM to be able to PHOTOSYNTHESISE	PHOSPHORUS (in the form of phosphates) to be able to RESPIRE

If any of these are unavailable the plant will soon start to look unhealthy.

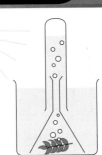

PHOTOSYNTHESIS AND RESPIRATION

Carbon dioxide is taken in by green plants during photosynthesis, but oxygen
is produced! This can be demonstrated using Canadian Pondweed in the experiment
shown opposite. What can also be shown is that the greater the amount of light
falling on the Pondweed, the faster it photosynthesises, and this can be measured by
counting the bubbles or timing how long it takes to fill the test tube with oxygen.
Plants, like all living organisms, need to use some oxygen for respiration. Thankfully, however, during normal
daylight the amount of oxygen they use is only a tiny proportion of the amount they produce. This means that
the oxygen in our atmosphere which is used up in respiration by animals and plants is replaced by the oxygen
produced in photosynthesis.

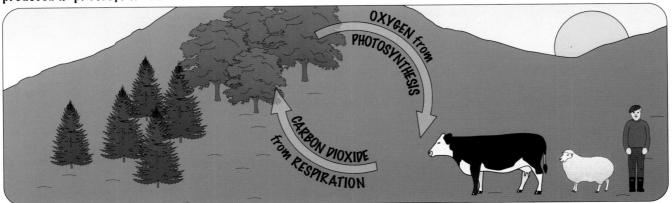

Happily this keeps the amounts of carbon dioxide and oxygen in the atmosphere remarkably constant:

Photosynthesis: **CARBON DIOXIDE + WATER + LIGHT ENERGY ⟶ GLUCOSE + OXYGEN**

Respiration: **GLUCOSE + OXYGEN ⟶ CARBON DIOXIDE + WATER + ENERGY**

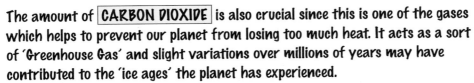

You'll see from the diagrams above that the two equations are each the reverse of the other one!

THE IMPORTANCE OF MAINTAINING THE BALANCE

Amazingly, the proportion of oxygen in the atmosphere (about ⅕th) is just about
perfect for life on this planet. Any less, and we wouldn't be able to respire as
effectively, but any more would make things burn more violently, turning the
planet into a fire hazard.

The amount of CARBON DIOXIDE is also crucial since this is one of the gases
which helps to prevent our planet from losing too much heat. It acts as a sort
of 'Greenhouse Gas' and slight variations over millions of years may have
contributed to the 'ice ages' the planet has experienced.

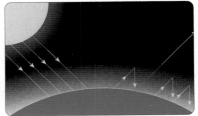

Cutting down our rainforests effectively reduces the planets 'lungs', allowing
carbon dioxide levels to increase. This may contribute to 'GLOBAL WARMING'
(See Environmental Chemistry) which could result in sea level rises and other
major environmental change.

KEYWORDS

Match the keywords from this unit to their definitions ...

BIOMASS	An element which is required for photosynthesis
CELLULOSE	A pale brown liquid, which is used to test for starch
STARCH	Green substance which is essential for photosynthesis
PHOTOSYNTHESIS	Structures in cells which contain chlorophyll and are the site of photosynthesis
CHLOROPLASTS	Specially adapted cells which absorb water and minerals
CHLOROPHYLL	Constituent of cell walls, which gives them their rigidity
IODINE	Mass of organic material
ROOT HAIR CELLS	An element used to produce protein in plants
NITROGEN	Element used by plants to enable respiration
POTASSIUM	Large insoluble molecule which provides glucose when broken down
PHOSPHORUS	Strands of tissue which extend from the roots of a plant to the leaves & consist of xylem and phloem
CARBON DIOXIDE	The process by which plants make food
GLOBAL WARMING	Gas which enables plants to photosynthesise
VASCULAR BUNDLES	Increase in average temperatures due to changes in the levels of atmospheric gases

PHOTOSYNTHESIS IN VARIEGATED LEAVES

Read this passage and then answer the questions below.

In variegated leaves, chlorophyll is only present in the parts of the leaves which are green. The remaining paler parts of the leaf contain no chlorophyll at all. Students investigating variegated leaves performed the following experiment. Firstly they removed a leaf from the variegated plant and placed it into boiling water for 30 seconds. Then they carefully removed it, blotted away excess water and placed it into very warm alcohol for 2-3 minutes. The alcohol was heated in a water bath. After this, they placed it back into hot water for a further minute or so before once again blotting away excess water. The leaf was then placed onto a white tile and iodine solution was dropped onto it until it was covered. When inspected, it was found that the parts of the leaf which had once been green were now blue-black in colour. This hadn't happened to the paler parts of the leaf.

A VARIEGATED LEAF

1. Why was the leaf placed into boiling water at the start of the experiment?
2. Why was the excess water blotted away before the leaf was placed in alcohol?
3. What was the reason for placing the leaf into alcohol?
4. Why was the alcohol heated in a water bath?
5. Why was the excess water blotted away before the leaf was covered in iodine?
6. What colour was the iodine solution originally?
7. What conclusion can you draw from this experiment?
8. What control experiment could you perform to reinforce your conclusion?

USING THE PRODUCTS OF PHOTOSYNTHESIS

Photosynthesis literally means 'making through ....' and is the process by which plants make their

.... It can only occur in the cells of .... plants, in the presence of light.

Apart from sunlight, three other things are needed: .... (found in chloroplasts), ... and

.... and .... are produced; the plant uses the ....

for .... and releases the .... into the atmosphere. Glucose can be converted into different

substances and subsequently used in other ways. The plant can change lots of single .... molecules

into chains of amino acids or proteins, which it then uses for new growth (................), it can convert sugars

into .... which is needed for the structure of .... walls or it can convert them into oils or

starch for ....

The process of photosynthesis is sometimes illustrated by an .... , this can be in the form of words or

.... If we were to use a symbol equation we would need to know the formulae for carbon dioxide

(......), water (......), ... ($C_6H_{12}O_6$) and oxygen (......).

EFFECT OF LIGHT ON CANADIAN PONDWEED

Some students decided to investigate the effect of light intensity on the production
of oxygen in Canadian Pondweed. They set up the experiment as shown and recorded
the results in the table below.

TIME TAKEN TO FILL TEST TUBE (mins)	20	35	55	90	150
DISTANCE FROM LAMP (cm)	20	40	60	80	100

Plot these results onto the graph paper provided and answer the questions below.

1. What conclusions can you draw from this graph?

   ....

   ....

   ....

   ....

2. How long would it take to fill the test tube at a
   distance of 90 cm?

   ....

3. At what distance would the test tube be filled in 75 minutes?

   ....

4. How long would it take at 0 cm?

   ....

Some pupils used monitoring equipment linked to a computer to measure the carbon dioxide concentration directly above a field of cabbages, during the month of July. They recorded the following data:

CO$_2$ (parts per 100,000)	34	35	40	34	30	29	28	28	29	30	32	33	34
TIME (24 hour clock)	00	02	04	06	08	10	12	14	16	18	20	22	24

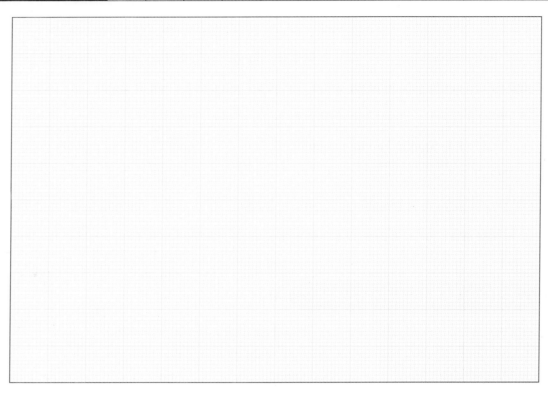

1. Plot the data onto the graph paper above. Clearly label your axes.

2. Over how long a period did the experiment take place?

....

3. At what time was the CO$_2$ concentration at its highest?

....

4. At what time was the CO$_2$ concentration at its lowest?

....

5. How would you explain your answers to 3 and 4?

....

....

6. At what time would you expect the oxygen concentration above the crop to be at its lowest?

....

7. Which key variables would need to be carefully controlled in order to make this a fair test?

....

....

FOOD CHAINS

These show that energy from the sun is 'trapped' by green plants which then pass energy on to the animals which eat them.

- The green plants are called the **PRODUCERS** because they produce the energy for their chain.
- The animals in the chain are called the **CONSUMERS** i.e. they eat things for their energy.
- Plant eating animals are called **HERBIVORES**. Animal-eating animals are called **CARNIVORES**.
- Animals which eat both animals and plants are called **OMNIVORES**.

PLANTS FOR FOOD

Humans try to intercept food chains at the producer stage (or the primary consumer in the case of animals for consumption) so that we eat the produce grown in our fields and gardens.

As you can see from the diagrams above, plants store the products of photosynthesis in a variety of ways. Some of these ways are designed to help the plant get through the winter while others are to help it to produce a new generation of plants by way of seeds. Either way,

... STORED AS STARCH IN STEMS AND/OR ROOTS

GLUCOSE from photosynthesis is ...   ... STORED AS STARCH AND OIL IN SEEDS

... STORED AS SUGAR IN FRUITS

MAN'S RELATIONSHIP WITH PLANTS

Humans use the fact that plants store food produced in photosynthesis as the basis for our farming industry. Harvesting crops when they are full of nutrients is the general strategy, regardless of whether the important part of the plant is above or below the ground.

WHEAT
APPLE
COCONUT

fruits and seeds

swollen stems

LEEK
RHUBARB
POTATO

PLANTS FOR FOOD

swollen roots

swollen leaves

CARROTS
RADISH
PARSNIPS

LETTUCE
CABBAGE
SPINACH

WHAT PLANTS COMPETE FOR

Plants compete for the four things shown below but they can also be affected by ...
HERBIVORES ... and ... HERBICIDES.

- If plants don't have sufficient space, they become crowded out.
- If they don't have sufficient light they can't photosynthesise.
- If they don't have sufficient water they will wilt and eventually die.
- If they don't have sufficient minerals they can't perform various chemical reactions, including photosynthesis ...

... Nitrogen, Potassium and Phosphorus are the main minerals a plant needs but there are others too. These are only needed in relatively small amounts. Nitrogen is used to help the plant make protein.

SPACE **LIGHT**

MINERALS **WATER**

USE OF FERTILISERS

Fertilisers can be bought in large bags and spread from the back of a tractor to provide all the necessary minerals a crop needs. But too much fertiliser can lead to it being washed off fields and into rivers.

WEEDS

Weeds are plants which aren't welcome in a particular area. They are 'wild' in the sense that they reproduce as ｂ they can without man's help. Weeds compete vigorously with other plants for the four things mentioned above.

USE OF HERBICIDES

Selective herbicides can be sprayed onto crops in order to kill particular weeds without harming the food plant that the farmer is growing. The problem with herbicides is that in removing the weeds, they also remove a vital food resource for many small animals. This has a knock-on effect in the FOOD WEB (see P.27) and results in other animals' food being seriously reduced. In some cases this can result in animals eating more of the food crop to compensate.

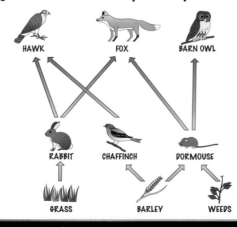

In the diagram alongside, removal of weeds to increase growing space for the barley, may remove a food source for the dormouse.

This may result in the dormouse population having to eat more of the barley crop to survive.

In addition, if the dormouse population declines the fox population also declines, resulting in more rabbits.

FOOD FOR THOUGHT

People buying vegetables 50 years ago would not recognise the vegetables in the shops today. It's not that they've changed shape or colour, it's just that nowadays they are in much better condition. Crop plants of 50 years ago nearly always showed signs of pest damage. Large areas of leaf would be eaten away. Nowadays, this would be unthinkable and any shop selling produce like that would quickly lose its customers. The reason for the improvement in the appearance of vegetables is simple ... increased use of PESTICIDES.

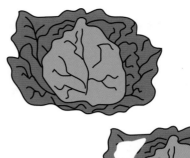

PROS AND CONS OF PESTICIDES

Plant pests actually compete with humans for crop plants, and the more they eat, the less there is available for humans. Field mice, caterpillars, aphids (greenfly), snails and slugs are just some of the pests that compete for crop plants. Remember, though, that each of these pests is a member of a very complicated food web which can be upset by the removal of a particular species.

In the case of the following food chain ...

LETTUCE   SNAILS   THRUSH

We can construct a pyramid of numbers to show the feeding relationship. Removing the snails will cause the lettuce crop to do well but may eliminate the thrushes. In the absence of a natural predator the snails may come back with a vengeance which would require the application of even more pesticide.

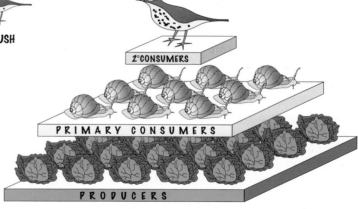

2°CONSUMERS

PRIMARY CONSUMERS

PRODUCERS

ADVANTAGES OF USING PESTICIDES	DISADVANTAGES OF USING PESTICIDES
• Increases CROP YIELD • Undamaged produce • Greater profitability	• Effect on the food web • Accumulation of pesticides within the food web (see next page)

PREDATOR/PREY CYCLES

The numbers of predators is closely linked to the numbers of their PREY. If the prey species declines, so will the predators. If the prey is killed by pesticides then there will be a dramatic fall in predator numbers.

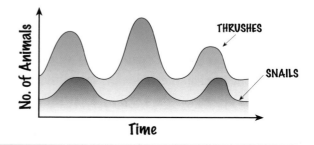

THRUSHES

SNAILS

No. of Animals

Time

ACCUMULATION OF TOXINS

Insecticides can be washed into streams and lakes where it forms a very dilute solution.

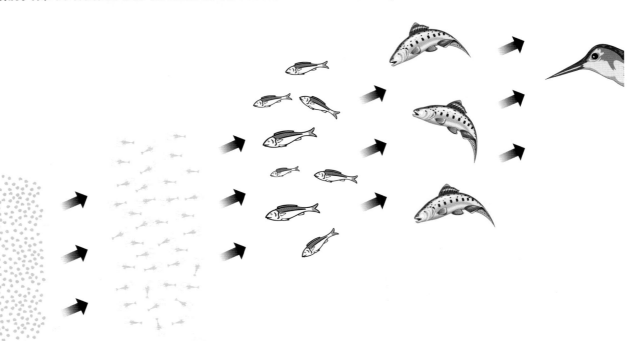

Microscopic plants take up the insecticide which doesn't harm them because it's a weak solution. Each microscopic animal however eats a huge number of these plants and therefore the concentration of insecticide increases. This happens again when small fish eat the microscopic animals, and again when the small fish are eaten by the larger fish. By the time the heron eats the larger fish the insecticide is concentrated enough to kill!! This is called BIOACCUMULATION, and only happens if the pesticide (or herbicide) isn't biodegradable ie. if it doesn't break down quickly after use.

Accumulation of toxins has had a serious affect on many species of bird life. Perhaps the classic example is the effect on the shell thickness of the eggs of Peregrine Falcons. This led to a massive decrease in their numbers.

SUSTAINABLE DEVELOPMENT

The aim of modern farming <u>should be</u> to produce the necessary amounts of crops as effectively as possible <u>with the minimal impact on the environment.</u> Organic farming sets out to do this by using only ORGANIC FERTILISER (eg. manure) and by using no herbicides or pesticides. However, decreased yields can make organic produce more expensive. Perhaps this is a price worth paying for the preservation of our environment and its wildlife. Another possible solution is to grow crop plants commercially under glass (in greenhouses) so that all aspects of growth can be controlled eg. amount of light, temperature, carbon dioxide level, minerals etc. Control of pests is a lot easier under these conditions, but they still manage to get in!! Of course for huge acreages of wheat etc. the cost of greenhousing would be too high.

THE LONG TERM VIEW

Our planet has limited resources and an ever increasing population which means that more and more food is going to be needed. If this means more and more inorganic fertiliser draining into our rivers and more use of pesticides on crops then we may eventually pay a high price!

KEYWORDS

Match the keywords from this unit to their definitions ...

SPACE	Substances which are needed for chemical reactions such as photosynthesis
LIGHT	A biological system made up of interlinking food chains
MINERALS	Plant-eating animals
WATER	Animals eaten by predators
HERBIVORES	Natural substances which can be added to soil to make it more fertile
HERBICIDES	Substances used to kill insects and other pests
FOOD WEB	An empty area which allows a plant to spread out
PESTICIDES	Provided by the sun to enable photosynthesis
CROP YIELD	Increase in concentration of chemicals within a food web
PREDATORS	Substances used to kill weeds
PREY	Liquid used by plant cells to keep them turgid and prevent wilting
BIOACCUMULATION	Amount of crop produced in a growing season
ORGANIC FERTILISER	Animals which eat other animals

ORGANIC FARMING

Read this passage and then answer the questions below.

In organic farming, all biodegradable waste material is composted and dug back into the soil. This means placing grass clippings, vegetable peelings and any prunings or dead plants in a large heap. The pile is turned over every now and then to make sure oxygen gets to all parts of it. After a few months you have excellent compost which adds nutrients to the soil as well as improving the soil structure.

Plants are grown only where the conditions suit them. If the plant likes acid soil in a partially shaded spot then it isn't placed in alkaline soil in full sun. Similarly, if the garden consists of mainly heavy clay soil then plants that prefer light, sandy, well-drained soils shouldn't be grown.

No artificial fertilisers or pesticides are used in organic farming. Biological controls, such as ladybirds to eat greenfly, are used and caterpillars, slugs and snails are picked off the plants by hand - although beer traps can be used for slugs. Bark chippings are used as a mulch to prevent weeds and in some areas the ground below the chippings is covered with black plastic sheeting.

1. What do we mean by 'biodegradable'?
2. Why is it important that the compost heap is turned over to allow oxygen to enter it?
3. How does digging compost back into the soil add nutrients?
4. Why don't organic gardeners change the pH of the soil to suit their plants?
5. How does covering the ground with bark chippings prevent weeds?
6. How might the appearance of lettuces grown organically differ from those grown using artificial fertilisers and pesticides?

EFFECT OF PESTICIDES ON FOOD WEBS

Chemically are often used to increase .... , improve appearance and remove competition. However, they also have negative effects on the .... and wildlife. Pesticides, a general name for insecticides, fungicides, ... and rodenticides are, as their name suggests, used to combat the problem of .... They have improved the appearance of our fruit and .... , which are no longer ravaged by pests such as caterpillars, ... (aphids) or field mice. However, killing populations of pests drastically affects .... webs. For example, imagine that thrushes eat insects and slugs; if all the .... were killed by the use of insecticides the thrushes' .... source would be severely .... and thus the numbers of thrushes would also be reduced. The consequence of this is that the .... would have .... predators and may, therefore, flourish and they will in turn eat .... of the food crop. .... can also be washed into .... and lakes where they are taken up by microscopic plants. At this stage they are very .... , but become more and more .... at every stage of the food chain. Eventually they become concentrated enough to .... This is called ....

EFFECT OF DDT ON PEREGRINES

Extensive use of the insecticide DDT during the 1950's resulted in a marked decline in the number of Peregrine Falcons. DDT cannot be excreted by animals which eat it and the accumulation of the poison in the Falcons caused them to produce very thin egg shells which often cracked, killing the chick.

The following data refers to the number of sightings of Peregrines since the use of such pesticides was banned.

YEAR	1964	1966	1968	1970	1972	1974	1976	1978	1980	1982	1984	1986
No. OF SIGHTINGS	4	5	4	6	7	6	12	11	15	22	43	76

1. Plot this data onto the graph paper provided.

2. What would have been the number of sightings in 1985?

3. In what year would the number of sightings have been approximately 33?

4. How many years did it take for the Peregrine population to treble?

5. Peregrines eat mainly small mammals, so why did an insecticide nearly wipe them out?

Pupils investigating the effect of artificial fertiliser on plant growth, planted lettuces in 6 marked off areas of their school field. Over a period of 8 weeks, the different areas were treated in the same way, however at the start of the period each area had different amounts of artificial fertiliser added. The data from this investigation is shown below.

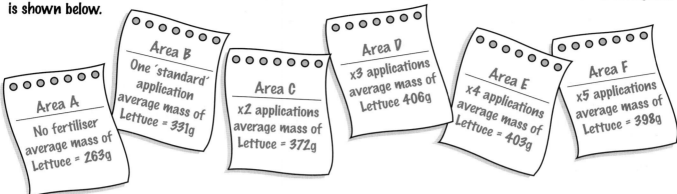

Area A — No fertiliser average mass of Lettuce = 263g

Area B — One 'standard' application average mass of Lettuce = 331g

Area C — x2 applications average mass of Lettuce = 372g

Area D — x3 applications average mass of Lettuce 406g

Area E — x4 applications average mass of Lettuce = 403g

Area F — x5 applications average mass of Lettuce = 398g

1. Arrange this data in a suitable table in the space provided below.

2. Plot this data onto the graph paper provided, choosing appropriate axes.

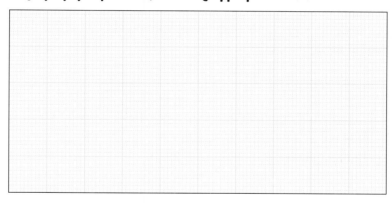

3. Why doesn't adding more fertiliser on Areas E and F make any difference?

....

....

4. What are the environmental dangers of using too much fertiliser?

....

....

5. What variables would need to be controlled to make this a fair test?

....

....

EXAMPLES OF ACID

The three main types you will use in the laboratory (in a DILUTE form) are:
HYDROCHLORIC ACID HCL, SULPHURIC ACID H_2SO_4, and NITRIC ACID HNO_3
Notice that they've all got hydrogen in them. This is true for all acids.

THE REACTION WITH METALS

Not all METALS react with ACIDS, but most do. Those that do react form A 'SALT' and HYDROGEN GAS.

$$\text{METAL} + \text{ACID} \longrightarrow \text{A 'SALT'} + \text{HYDROGEN}$$

For example ...

| ZINC | + | HYDROCHLORIC ACID | ⟶ | ZINC CHLORIDE | + | HYDROGEN |

$$Zn_{(s)} + 2HCl_{(aq)} \longrightarrow ZnCl_{2(aq)} + H_{2(g)}$$

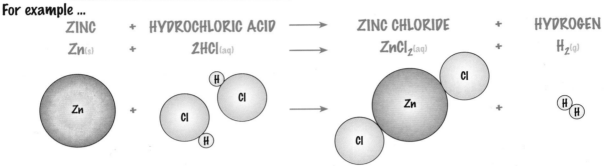

All that has happened is that the zinc has joined with the chlorine atoms to form a salt, zinc chloride.
At the same time hydrogen is released. In a reaction between a metal and an acid, the product formed by the combination of the metal and the 'non-hydrogen' part of the acid is always called A SALT.

DIFFERENCES IN THE REACTIONS

Some metals react more vigorously than others depending on how high up in the Reactivity Series they are.
(See P.41). Some don't react at all.

MAGNESIUM   ALUMINIUM   IRON   COPPER

Also, metals react in different ways with different acids.
For instance, calcium reacts with hydrochloric acid to produce ...

MAGNESIUM   +   HYDROCHLORIC ACID   ⟶   MAGNESIUM CHLORIDE   +   HYDROGEN

But also, calcium reacts with sulphuric acid to produce ...

MAGNESIUM   +   SULPHURIC ACID   ⟶   MAGNESIUM SULPHATE   +   HYDROGEN

HYDROCHLORIC ACID PRODUCES CHLORIDES. SULPHURIC ACID PRODUCES SULPHATES.

TESTING FOR THE PRODUCTS OF THE REACTION

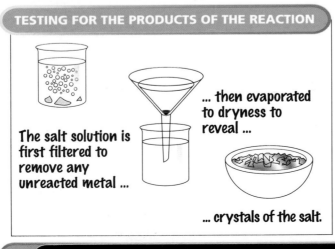

... then evaporated to dryness to reveal ...

The salt solution is first filtered to remove any unreacted metal ...

... crystals of the salt.

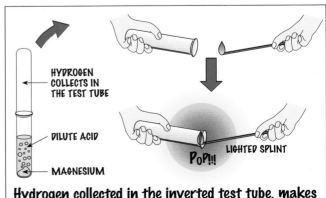

HYDROGEN COLLECTS IN THE TEST TUBE

DILUTE ACID

MAGNESIUM

LIGHTED SPLINT

POP!!!

Hydrogen collected in the inverted test tube, makes a SQUEAKY POP when lit.

EXAMPLES OF METAL CARBONATES

METAL CARBONATES are made up of a particular metal combined with carbon and oxygen. The carbon and oxygen are combined together as a carbonate group which is made from one carbon atom and three oxygen atoms.

MAGNESIUM CARBONATE

$MgCO_3$

CALCIUM CARBONATE

$CaCO_3$

THE REACTION WITH ACIDS

METAL CARBONATES react with DILUTE ACID to form ...

1. ... A 'SALT'. Again this is a metal compound formed because a reaction has taken place with an acid.

2. ... CARBON DIOXIDE. Bubbles of carbon dioxide gas are formed which is an indication that a chemical reaction has taken place.

3. ... WATER.

Another indication that a reaction has taken place is that heat is given off and the test tube containing the metal carbonate and acid becomes warm.

In general ...

METAL CARBONATE + ACID ⟶ A 'SALT' + CARBON DIOXIDE + WATER

For example ...

CALCIUM CARBONATE + HYDROCHLORIC ACID ⟶ CALCIUM CHLORIDE + CARBON DIOXIDE + WATER

$$CaCO_{3(s)} + 2HCl_{(aq)} \longrightarrow CaCl_{2(aq)} + CO_{2(g)} + H_2O_{(l)}$$

All that has happened is that the calcium has joined with the chlorine atoms to form a salt, calcium chloride. At the same time the carbonate group and the hydrogen atoms have rearranged themselves to form carbon dioxide and water.

Metal carbonates react in different ways with different acids.

HYDROCHLORIC ACID PRODUCES CHLORIDES. SULPHURIC ACID PRODUCES SULPHATES.

TESTING FOR CARBON DIOXIDE GAS PRODUCED IN THE REACTION

Carbon dioxide turns LIMEWATER 'MILKY'. This can easily be shown by using the following apparatus.

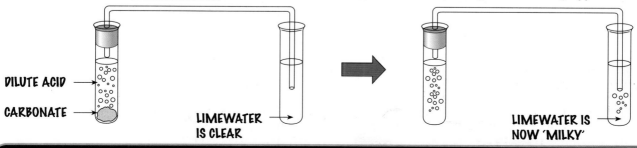

DILUTE ACID

CARBONATE

LIMEWATER IS CLEAR

LIMEWATER IS NOW 'MILKY'

EXAMPLES OF METAL OXIDES

Metal oxides (and hydroxides) are sometimes called BASES . Metal oxides consist simply of the metal plus one or more oxygen atoms.

 SODIUM OXIDE Na_2O

 ALUMINIUM OXIDE Al_2O_3

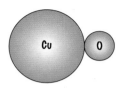 COPPER OXIDE CuO

THE REACTION WITH ACIDS

METAL OXIDES react with DILUTE ACID to form ...

1. ... A 'SALT' . Again this is a metal compound produced because a reaction has taken place with an acid.

2. ... WATER .

In general ...

$$\text{METAL OXIDE + ACID} \longrightarrow \text{A 'SALT' + WATER}$$

For example ...

| COPPER OXIDE | + | SULPHURIC ACID | $\longrightarrow$ | COPPER SULPHATE | + | WATER |
| $CuO_{(s)}$ | + | $H_2SO_{4(aq)}$ | $\longrightarrow$ | $CuSO_{4(aq)}$ | + | $H_2O_{(l)}$ |

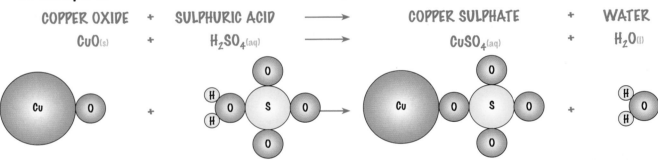

All that has happened is that the copper has joined with the sulphate (SO_4) to form a salt, copper sulphate. At the same time, the hydrogen atoms and the remaining oxygen atom have joined together to form a water molecule. This time there are no bubbles since no gas is given off.

Metal oxides react in different ways with different acids.

HYDROCHLORIC ACID PRODUCES CHLORIDES. SULPHURIC ACID PRODUCES SULPHATES.

TESTING FOR THE PRODUCTS OF THE REACTION

During the course of this reaction, a blue solution of copper sulphate is formed. This can be filtered from the excess copper oxide and then evaporated to dryness to produce blue crystals.

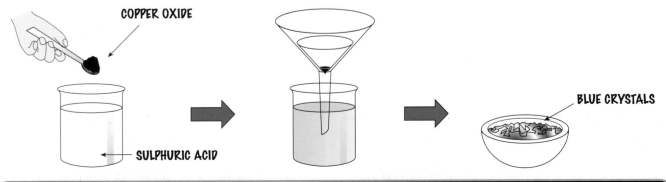

COPPER OXIDE

SULPHURIC ACID

BLUE CRYSTALS

EXAMPLES OF ALKALIS

The THREE main types you will use in the laboratory (in a DILUTE form) are:
SODIUM HYDROXIDE NaOH, POTASSIUM HYDROXIDE KOH and CALCIUM HYDROXIDE Ca(OH)$_2$
Notice that they've all got OH in them. This is true of all alkalis. An ALKALI is the name given to a metal oxide
or hydroxide that is soluble in water.

NEUTRALISATION

A NEUTRALISATION reaction occurs when an acid and an alkali 'cancel each other out' to produce a
NEUTRAL solution, ie. one with a pH of 7.

ACID (containing universal indicator)   pH2

ALKALI (containing universal indicator)   pH13   pH7   NEUTRAL SOLUTION

Acids react with alkalis to form ...
1. ... A 'SALT' .
2. ... WATER .

ACID + ALKALI ⟶ A 'SALT' + WATER

For example ...

| SODIUM HYDROXIDE | + | HYDROCHLORIC ACID | ⟶ | SODIUM CHLORIDE | + | WATER |
| NaOH$_{(aq)}$ | + | HCl$_{(aq)}$ | ⟶ | NaCl$_{(aq)}$ | + | H$_2$O$_{(l)}$ |

All that has happened is that the sodium has joined with the chlorine to form a salt, sodium chloride.
At the same time, the hydrogen atoms and oxygen atoms have formed water.
In neutralisation reactions, the salt formed depends on the metal in the alkali and the type of acid used.

HYDROCHLORIC ACID PRODUCES CHLORIDES. SULPHURIC ACID PRODUCES SULPHATES.

PREPARING SALTS   eg. sodium chloride, NaCl

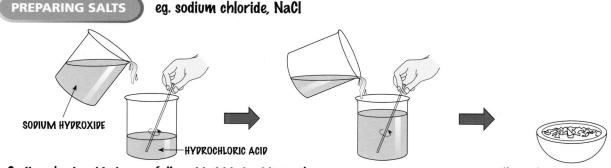

SODIUM HYDROXIDE

HYDROCHLORIC ACID

Sodium hydroxide is carefully added bit by bit to the
hydrochloric acid. It is continuously stirred and a drop
of the solution is occasionally removed using the glass
rod and its pH tested using universal indicator paper.
This carries on until the solution has a pH of 7.

The solution is evaporated
to leave behind crystals of
SODIUM CHLORIDE
ie. common salt.

KEYWORDS

Match the keywords from this unit to their definitions ...

ACID	The lightest element, it is a colourless and odourless gas
METAL	Colourless gas made up of carbon and oxygen
SALT	Compound consisting of a metal combined with carbon and oxygen
HYDROGEN	An oxide or hydroxide of a metal
METAL CARBONATE	Solution which turns milky when carbon dioxide is bubbled through it
CARBON DIOXIDE	Reaction that occurs when an acid and alkali react to form a 'salt' and water
WATER	An element which is usually a good conductor of electricity and heat
LIMEWATER	Compound consisting of a metal combined with oxygen
METAL OXIDE	Neither acid nor alkali, a pH of 7
BASE	A substance which contains hydrogen and has a pH below 7
ALKALI	Colourless liquid consisting of hydrogen and oxygen
NEUTRALISATION	A soluble base
NEUTRAL	Metal compound formed when a reaction takes place with an acid

THREE MYSTERY SUBSTANCES

Read this passage and then answer the questions below.

Three different substances A, B and C were placed in test tubes in the form of ground-up powder. Three different liquids were then added to each of the three test tubes. Tube A produced bubbles of gas which, when collected and brought close to a lighted splint caused a 'squeaky pop'. Tube B also produced bubbles which, when passed through limewater, caused it to go milky. Tube C produced no bubbles. After these substances had been allowed to react, all three were evaporated to dryness to reveal three crystalline substances. Substance A had produced magnesium chloride, substance B had produced zinc sulphate and substance C had produced iron chloride.

1. Which gas did substance A produce?
2. Which gas did substance B produce?
3. What is the general name given to all three substances produced after the liquids had been evaporated?
4. Which liquid was added to tube A?
5. Which liquid was added to tube B?
6. Which liquid was added to tube C?
7. Suggest what substance A might have been?
8. Suggest what substance B might have been?
9. Suggest what substance C might have been?
10. Write down a word equation for the reaction involving substance A.
11. Write down a word equation for the reaction involving substance B.
12. Write down a word equation for the reaction involving substance C.

REACTIONS OF ACIDS

Metals that react with .... form a salt and hydrogen eg. aluminium and ....

will react to form aluminium chloride and hydrogen. To test for the salt, filter the solution to remove any unreacted

.... and then .... to dryness to leave behind the salt. To test for hydrogen: a

.... splint inverted into a test tube of hydrogen makes a squeaky pop.

Metal carbonates react with acids to form a .... , carbon dioxide and ....

eg. calcium carbonate and sulphuric acid will react to form .... , carbon dioxide and

.... To test for carbon dioxide: .... turns milky when carbon dioxide is bubbled

through it. Metal oxides react with acids to form a .... and .... eg. iron oxide will react

with hydrochloric acid to form .... and ....

A neutralisation reaction occurs when an acid and an .... cancel each other out to produce a

.... solution. In general, an acid reacts with an .... to form a .... and water

eg. .... hydroxide will react with .... acid to form calcium chloride and ....

In all of these reactions: .... acid produces chlorides and .... acid produces sulphates.

REACTION OF CARBONATES WITH ACIDS

Some pupils used this apparatus to measure the total volume of gas
given off every 20 secs, when excess dilute sulphuric acid was added
to calcium carbonate. The volume of gas was measured using a
graduated gas jar. Here are their results.

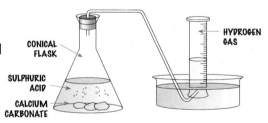

CONICAL FLASK

HYDROGEN GAS

SULPHURIC ACID

CALCIUM CARBONATE

VOLUME OF GAS PRODUCED (cm³)	0	200	350	450	520	560	580	580	580
TIME (secs)	0	20	40	60	80	100	120	140	160

1. Plot a graph of their results.

2. Name the gas given off in the reaction.

   ....

3. Write down a word equation for the reaction
   taking place.

   ....

4. Why was there no gas given off after 120 secs?

   ....

   ....

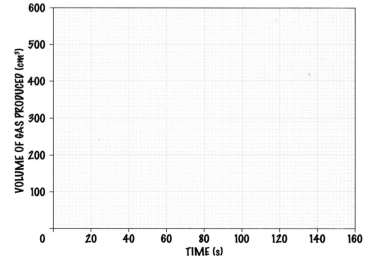

Jane was asked to investigate if there was a link between the concentration of an acid and the volume needed to neutralise 50cm³ of alkali. She used a piece of apparatus called a burette to add the acid to the alkali until she got a neutral solution. She then repeated the investigation using four other acids whose strength was gradually increased compared to the standard strength of the first acid which she used ie. the second acid was twice (2x) as strong, the third acid was three (3x) times as strong etc.

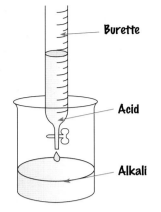

1. How would Jane measure the pH of the solution and what would she observe?

....

2. What factors must Jane have kept the same in order to make this a fair test?

....

3. Her results were as follows.

STRENGTH OF ACID	VOLUME OF ACID ADDED (cm3)
1x	100
2x	49
3x	33
4x	26
5x	21

Plot these on the graph paper provided.

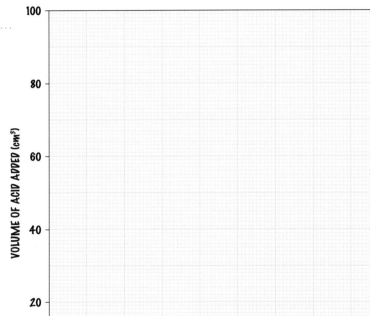

4. What conclusion could Jane come to from her results?

....

....

5. Would the volume of alkali she used affect her results? Explain your answer.

....

....

6. Would the strength of the alkali she used affect her results? Explain your answer.

....

....

7. What safety precautions should she have followed during her investigation?

DIFFERENT CHARACTERISTICS OF METALS

Most METALS are SHINY, and are good CONDUCTORS of HEAT and ELECTRICITY, but the melting points and hardness of metals varies a great deal. This means that different metals have characteristics which make them suitable for different jobs.

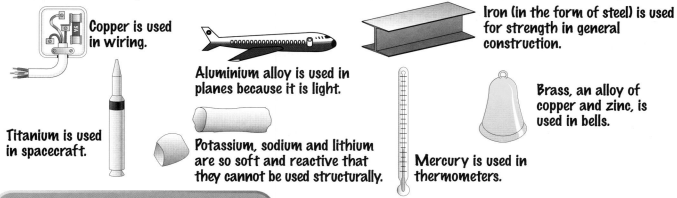

Copper is used in wiring.

Aluminium alloy is used in planes because it is light.

Iron (in the form of steel) is used for strength in general construction.

Brass, an alloy of copper and zinc, is used in bells.

Titanium is used in spacecraft.

Potassium, sodium and lithium are so soft and reactive that they cannot be used structurally.

Mercury is used in thermometers.

REACTIONS OF METALS WITH OXYGEN

OXYGEN forms 21% of the air around us.

This means that metals that react with oxygen will do so if they are left in air.

AN IRON NAIL RUSTS   A SILVER RING DULLS   A COPPER PIPE DARKENS   AN ALUMINIUM FRAME GOES GREY

Some metals, for example gold, do not react with oxygen at all and as a result they are found in their pure form and not as ores. Other metals, for example potassium, are so reactive that a freshly cut shiny surface of the metal becomes dull within seconds, when it is exposed to air.

Metals that react with oxygen form OXIDES ...

$$\text{METAL} + \text{OXYGEN} \longrightarrow \text{METAL OXIDE}$$

For example ...

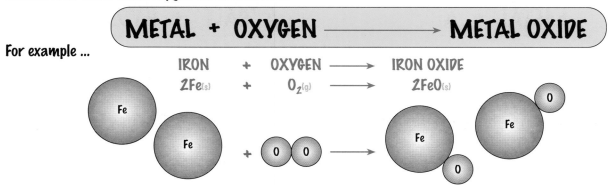

IRON $\quad + \quad$ OXYGEN $\longrightarrow$ IRON OXIDE

$2Fe_{(s)} \quad + \quad O_{2(g)} \longrightarrow 2FeO_{(s)}$

All that has happened is that two iron atoms have combined with a molecule of oxygen. Some metals react more vigorously than others depending on how high up the Reactivity Series they are (see P.41). Heating the metal will increase the rate at which it reacts with oxygen to the extent that it may even burn.

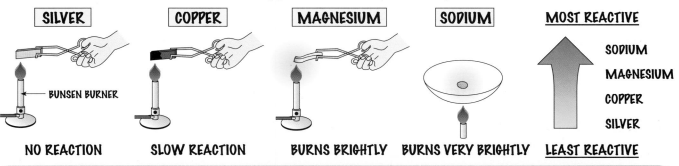

SILVER	COPPER	MAGNESIUM	SODIUM	MOST REACTIVE

BUNSEN BURNER

SODIUM
MAGNESIUM
COPPER
SILVER

NO REACTION   SLOW REACTION   BURNS BRIGHTLY   BURNS VERY BRIGHTLY   LEAST REACTIVE

REACTIONS OF METALS WITH WATER

Metals that react with water form either METAL HYDROXIDES or METAL OXIDES and HYDROGEN ...

METAL + WATER ⟶ METAL HYDROXIDE + HYDROGEN
(or METAL OXIDE)

For example ...

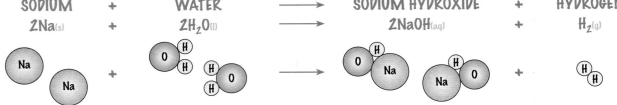

| SODIUM | + | WATER | ⟶ | SODIUM HYDROXIDE | + | HYDROGEN |
| $2Na_{(s)}$ | + | $2H_2O_{(l)}$ | ⟶ | $2NaOH_{(aq)}$ | + | $H_{2(g)}$ |

The hydroxide formed is of course ALKALINE with a pH between 8 and 14.

Some metals react more vigorously than others with WATER ...

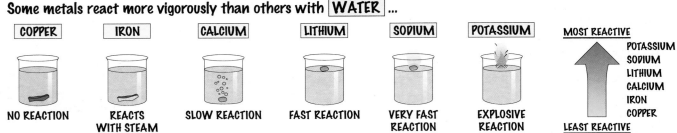

| COPPER | IRON | CALCIUM | LITHIUM | SODIUM | POTASSIUM | MOST REACTIVE |
| NO REACTION | REACTS WITH STEAM | SLOW REACTION | FAST REACTION | VERY FAST REACTION | EXPLOSIVE REACTION | POTASSIUM
SODIUM
LITHIUM
CALCIUM
IRON
COPPER
LEAST REACTIVE |

The THREE 'alkali metals,' lithium, sodium and potassium react very vigorously. Lithium bubbles away producing hydrogen; sodium produces so much hydrogen that it can be lit with a lighted splint; while potassium bursts into flame immediately and often explosively.

REACTIONS OF METALS WITH ACID

Metals that react with DILUTE ACID form A SALT (see P.32) plus HYDROGEN.

METAL + ACID ⟶ A 'SALT' + HYDROGEN

For example ...

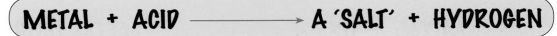

| MAGNESIUM | + | SULPHURIC ACID | ⟶ | MAGNESIUM SULPHATE | + | HYDROGEN |
| $Mg_{(s)}$ | + | $H_2SO_{4(aq)}$ | ⟶ | $MgSO_{4(aq)}$ | + | $H_{2(g)}$ |

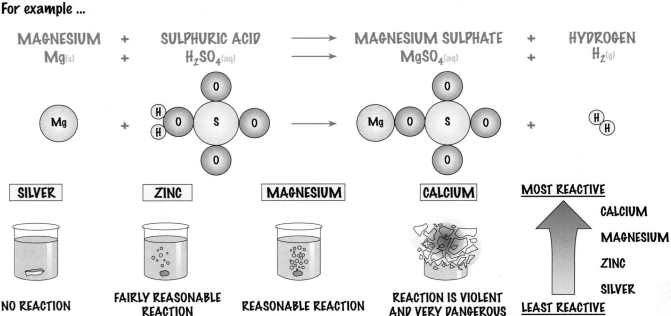

| SILVER | ZINC | MAGNESIUM | CALCIUM | MOST REACTIVE |
| NO REACTION | FAIRLY REASONABLE REACTION | REASONABLE REACTION | REACTION IS VIOLENT AND VERY DANGEROUS | CALCIUM
MAGNESIUM
ZINC
SILVER
LEAST REACTIVE |

The order of REACTIVITY is the same no matter which acid is used. However, more reactive metals tend to produce heat during the reaction - so beware!

ARRANGING METALS IN ORDER OF THEIR REACTIVITY

The information on the previous two pages on how metals react with OXYGEN, WATER and DILUTE ACID, can be used to produce a table of reactivity or a REACTIVITY SERIES .

The most reactive element is placed at the top of the series and the other elements follow in order of their reactivity down to the least reactive.

REACTIVITY SERIES OF SOME COMMON METALS

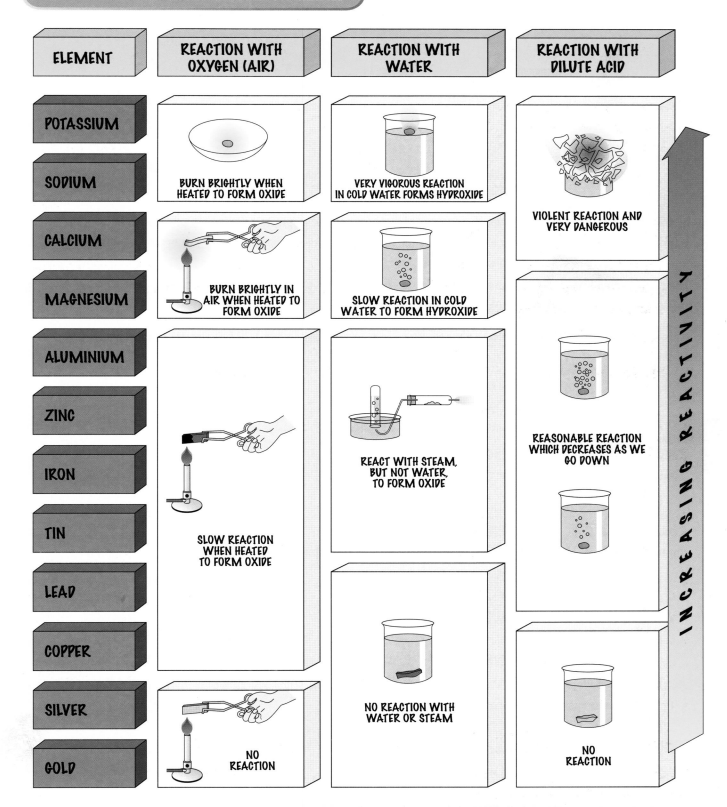

ELEMENT	REACTION WITH OXYGEN (AIR)	REACTION WITH WATER	REACTION WITH DILUTE ACID
POTASSIUM	BURN BRIGHTLY WHEN HEATED TO FORM OXIDE	VERY VIGOROUS REACTION IN COLD WATER FORMS HYDROXIDE	VIOLENT REACTION AND VERY DANGEROUS
SODIUM			
CALCIUM	BURN BRIGHTLY IN AIR WHEN HEATED TO FORM OXIDE	SLOW REACTION IN COLD WATER TO FORM HYDROXIDE	REASONABLE REACTION WHICH DECREASES AS WE GO DOWN
MAGNESIUM			
ALUMINIUM	SLOW REACTION WHEN HEATED TO FORM OXIDE	REACT WITH STEAM, BUT NOT WATER, TO FORM OXIDE	
ZINC			
IRON			
TIN			
LEAD		NO REACTION WITH WATER OR STEAM	
COPPER			
SILVER	NO REACTION		NO REACTION
GOLD			

INCREASING REACTIVITY

REACTIVITY OF METALS

The first three pages of this unit show how metals react differently with oxygen, water and dilute acid. Their order of reactivity as shown in the Reactivity Series on the previous page enables us to make predictions regarding chemical reactions between metals and metal salts.

DISPLACEMENT REACTIONS

In a DISPLACEMENT REACTION , a more reactive metal displaces a less reactive metal from a solution of one of its salts. For instance iron can displace copper from a solution of copper sulphate.

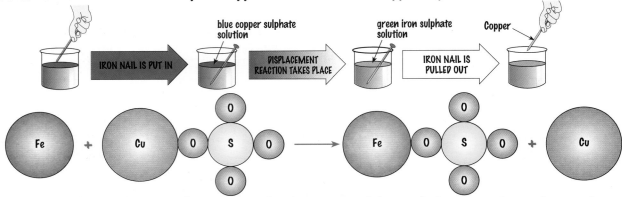

blue copper sulphate solution
IRON NAIL IS PUT IN
DISPLACEMENT REACTION TAKES PLACE
green iron sulphate solution
IRON NAIL IS PULLED OUT
Copper

In this reaction, the iron displaces the copper in the blue copper sulphate solution, to produce pale green iron sulphate. The displaced copper coats the iron nail, and some falls to the bottom of the beaker.

IRON + COPPER SULPHATE ⟶ IRON SULPHATE + COPPER

The reason this happens is because iron is higher in the Reactivity Series than copper.

• There's one incredibly important rule to remember ...

> **IF THE PURE METAL IS HIGHER IN THE REACTIVITY SERIES THAN THE METAL IN THE COMPOUND, THEN DISPLACEMENT WILL HAPPEN.**

SOME MORE EXAMPLES OF DISPLACEMENT

EXAMPLE 1. ZINC + COPPER SULPHATE SOLUTION ⟶ ZINC SULPHATE SOLUTION + COPPER

Remember the 'Rule', which is HIGHER in the Reactivity Series?
Zinc is higher so it displaces the Copper forming zinc sulphate. ✓

EXAMPLE 2. COPPER + MAGNESIUM NITRATE SOLUTION ⟶ NO CHANGE

Remember the 'Rule', which is HIGHER in the Reactivity Series?
Copper is lower in the series than magnesium and so no reaction takes place. ✗

A DISPLACEMENT REACTION IN ACTION

MAGNESIUM RIBBON 'FUSE'
ALUMINIUM POWDER AND IRON OXIDE

• When a mixture of ALUMINIUM POWDER ...

... and IRON OXIDE is heated ...

... an extremely VIGOROUS DISPLACEMENT REACTION takes place with the HEAT RELEASED ...

... being great enough to melt the displaced iron. This happens because aluminium is higher in the Series than iron.

• This particular displacement reaction ...

... is called the THERMIT REACTION .

• The MOLTEN IRON can then be used ...

SMALL PLUG OF IRON REMAINS

... for various purposes, eg. to weld together railway tracks.

ALUMINIUM + IRON OXIDE ⟶ ALUMINIUM OXIDE + IRON

KEYWORDS

Match the keywords from this unit to their definitions ...

METALS	A colourless gas, found in all acids
OXYGEN	Metal compound formed when a metal reacts with an acid
METAL OXIDE	Refers to a substance which has been watered down
METAL HYDROXIDE	When a more reactive metal replaces a less reactive metal from a solution of one of its salts
HYDROGEN	A colourless and odourless gas that makes up around one-fifth of air
A SALT	An arrangement of metals in order of how vigorously they react with oxygen, water and dilute acid
WATER	Compound consisting of a metal plus oxygen and hydrogen
DILUTE	Most are shiny and good conductors of electricity and heat
REACTIVITY	Displacement reaction that takes place between aluminium and iron oxide
REACTIVITY SERIES	A neutral substance, proper name is hydrogen oxide
DISPLACEMENT REACTION	Formed when a metal reacts with oxygen
THERMIT REACTION	A measure of how vigorously one substance reacts with another

REACTIVITY OF METALS

Read this passage and then answer the questions below.

Martinium reacts violently with water compared to wellenium which reacts fairly slowly. Ironium reacts quite well with dilute acid compared to sullivanium, which doesn't react at all. Longium, like sullivanium, forms an oxide when heated in air but sculthium doesn't react with oxygen at all. Longium reacts with steam to form an oxide whereas sullivanium doesn't. Wellenium displaces ironium from a solution of one of its salts.

1. Write down the 6 metals in order of their reactivity.

2. Which metals could be displaced by longium?

3. Which metals would displace ironium?

4. Which metal would be expected to exist naturally?

5. Which metal would need to be stored under oil?

6. Which of these metals should never be reacted with dilute acid?

7. Would you expect longium to react with dilute acid?

8. How would you expect martinium and wellenium to react with air when heated?

METALS AND THEIR REACTIONS

Different metals have different characteristics which make them useful eg. copper is a good ....

of electricity and is therefore used in wiring; iron, in the form of ...., is used for construction because

of its ....

Metals that react with oxygen form .... eg. magnesium would react with oxygen to

form .... Those that react with water form either .... or ....

with the production of .... gas, eg. calcium would react with water to form ....

.... and ....

Metals that react with acid form a .... and .... eg. zinc would react with hydrochloric acid

to form .... and ....

Some metals react more vigorously than others and this is used as the basis for the ....

The .... reactive metal is placed at the top with the .... reactive at the bottom.

A displacement reaction occurs when a .... reactive metal displaces a .... reactive metal from

a solution of one of its .... The displacement reaction between aluminium powder and iron oxide is

known as the .... reaction.

DISPLACEMENT

Six metals A, B, C, D, E and F were each added in turn to a solution of one of their salts.
The bar graph below shows the number of displacement reactions that took place for each metal.

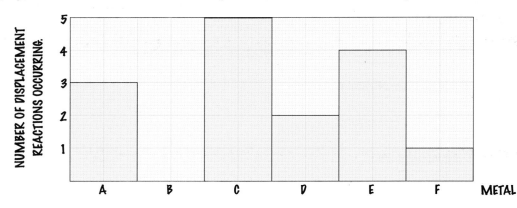

1. Which metal is the most reactive? Explain your choice.

....

....

2. Complete the following table placing a ✓
where a displacement reaction has occurred
and a ✗ where one hasn't.

METAL SALT	METAL					
	A	B	C	D	E	F
A						
B						
C						
D						
E						
F						

Tom was asked to carry out an investigation into the rate at which seven different metals (iron, aluminium, tin, magnesium, zinc, lead and copper) produce hydrogen when added to dilute hydrochloric acid. The equipment he used is shown in the diagram. He added a metal to the acid and then timed how long it took to collect a test tube full of hydrogen.

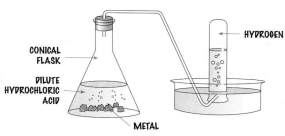

1. Give four variables that he should control in order to make this a fair test.

....

....

2. His results are as follows. He chose not to use copper.

METAL	IRON	ALUMINIUM	TIN	MAGNESIUM	ZINC	LEAD
TIME (s)	32	16	43	10	36	58

Draw a graph to show his results in order of most reactive to least reactive.

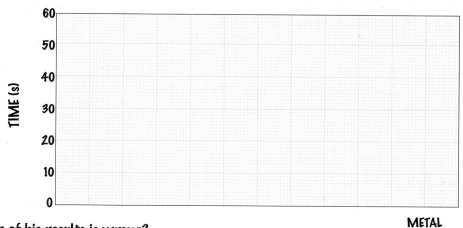

3. Which one of his results is wrong?
   Explain how you came to your choice and write down approximately what result he should have got.

....

....

....

4. Give as many reasons as possible as to why Tom may have obtained a wrong result.

....

....

5. What conclusion can Tom come to from his results?

....

....

6. Explain why Tom chose not to use copper when carrying out his investigation.

....

....

STRUCTURE OF THE SOIL

Most of the earth's landmass has a covering of soil. It can be less than 1cm thick on rocky outcrops or many cm. thick on cultivated land. Soils can vary enormously but in general they are made up of the following things ...

1. SMALL FRAGMENTS OF ROCK

These have been produced by weathering and erosion of rock or buildings. Their size, colour and shape will vary and affect the texture of the soil, by determining the amount of air spaces in it.

These rock particles have usually been deposited at sometime in the past as SEDIMENTS from rivers, and streams. Similar sized particles are often deposited at the same time.

2. LIVING AND DEAD VEGETATION

The dead organic material, from the remains of animals and plants, helps to give soil its structure making it easier to dig, and the nutrients in it improve the fertility of the soil. The ability of the soil to hold water is also improved. The roots of the plants help to hold the top soil together and prevent soil erosion by wind and rain.

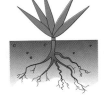

3. WATER

Plants need water and the nutrients dissolved in it. These nutrients are from the organic matter but in some cases can be added to the soil artificially.

4. ANIMALS

Bacteria and fungi in the soil help to break down organic matter so that minerals become available to plants. Earthworms help to aerate the soil and to bring down organic matter from the surface.

PLANTS AND SOIL pH

Different plants prefer different types of soil. Some prefer light, well-drained soils while others prefer heavier, clayey soils which hold water. However, perhaps the most critical thing is not the soil's structure but the soil's pH. Most soils range from pH4 to pH8.

Pieris, Camellia, Heather, Berberis, Azalea

	SLIGHTLY ACIDIC		NEUTRAL	SLIGHTLY ALKALINE
4	5	6	7	8

Clematis, Daphne, Alpines

Soil testing kits can be used to test the pH of the soil.

IF THE SOIL IS TOO ACIDIC ...
... then LIME in the form of CALCIUM CARBONATE (limestone) which works slowly, or CALCIUM HYDROXIDE (quicklime) which works quickly can be used to NEUTRALISE the acidity of the soil.

IF THE SOIL IS TOO ALKALINE ...
... then sphagnum moss PEAT can be dug into it or a proprietary acidifier can be used. In the garden, tea leaves are a good source of acid for acid loving plants!

HOW ACID RAIN IS PRODUCED

1. CARBON DIOXIDE

This exists naturally in the atmosphere and is also produced when FOSSIL FUELS are burned.

2. SULPHUR DIOXIDE

This is produced when FOSSIL FUELS are burned and also through VOLCANIC ACTIVITY.

3. OXIDES OF NITROGEN (compounds containing nitrogen and oxygen)

These are produced when FOSSIL FUELS are burned and also given out by the EXHAUSTS OF MOTOR VEHICLES.

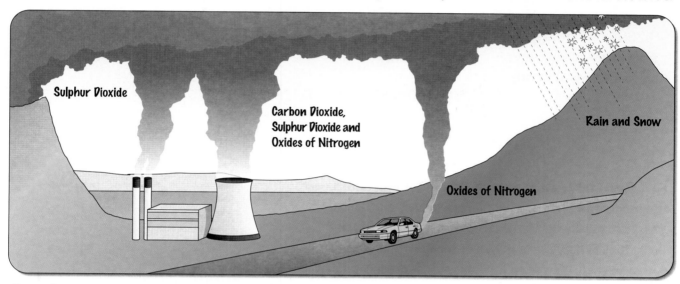

Sulphur Dioxide

Carbon Dioxide, Sulphur Dioxide and Oxides of Nitrogen

Rain and Snow

Oxides of Nitrogen

These three pollutant gases dissolve in water in the atmosphere to form ACIDIC SOLUTIONS in clouds ...

... they fall back to Earth as either ACID RAIN or possibly ACID SNOW.

The burning of fuels in power stations and factories produces over 30 million tonnes of sulphur dioxide every year in the United Kingdom. The sulphur is an impurity in coal and reacts with oxygen to form sulphur dioxide ...

$$S_{(s)} + O_{2(g)} \longrightarrow SO_{2(g)}$$

sulphur   oxygen   sulphur dioxide

sulphur   +   oxygen   →   sulphur dioxide

This sulphur dioxide reacts with water vapour in the atmosphere ...

$$SO_{2(g)} + H_2O_{(l)} \longrightarrow H_2SO_{3(aq)}$$

sulphur dioxide   water   sulphurous acid

sulphur dioxide   +   water   →   sulphurous acid

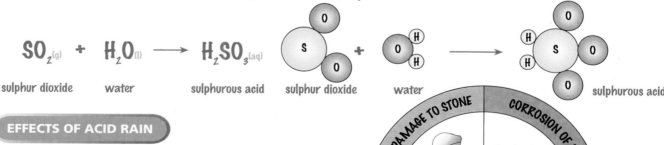

EFFECTS OF ACID RAIN

ACID RAIN usually has a pH of between 3-5 depending upon the amount of pollutants dissolved in it. This makes it easily capable of slowly dissolving carbonate-containing rocks such as limestone, marble and chalk, and also of reacting with, and eventually corroding unpainted metal. Trees and lakes can also be badly affected due to the low pH.

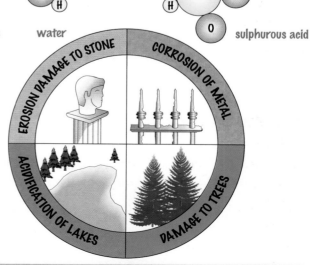

EROSION DAMAGE TO STONE

CORROSION OF METAL

ACIDIFICATION OF LAKES

DAMAGE TO TREES

AIR QUALITY is affected by many things; nearly all of them are man-made ...

PARTICULATES ...
from dust and products of combustion.

HYDROCARBONS ...
from combustion in factories and cars.

OXIDES OF NITROGEN ...
from vehicle engines and combustion in factories.

COMPOUNDS OF LEAD ...
from engines of motor vehicles.

OZONE ...
from action of sun's rays on many other pollutants.

AIR QUALITY
is affected by ...

POLLEN ...
from flowering plants in Summer.

CARBON MONOXIDE ...
from vehicle exhausts and many heavy industries.

SULPHUR DIOXIDE ...
from combustion of fuels in power stations and factories.

Environmental agencies monitor the level of pollutants in our atmosphere and this information is available on teletext. These are usually measured in 'parts per million' (p.p.m.). Some typical figures are shown in the table alongside. Although these may seem tiny amounts, it doesn't take huge concentrations to cause environmental problems.

DATE	15.04.2001
SULPHUR DIOXIDE	85 p.p.m.
OXIDES OF NITROGEN	52 p.p.m.
OZONE	80 p.p.m.
LEAD	12 p.p.m.
POLLEN COUNT IS LOW ...	

WAYS OF REDUCING THE PROBLEM

Scientists have been trying to reduce the pollutants in our atmosphere for many years, and with some success. However, most of the remedies rely on new technology and come at a considerable cost. If we are to protect the environment then this is a cost we must be prepared to pay.

HYDROCARBONS	• Use of more efficient engines which completely burn the fuel. • Catalytic converters to convert hydrocarbons to CO_2	
LEAD COMPOUNDS	• Stop adding lead compounds to petrol. Post 1990 vehicles in the UK can run on lead-free.	LEAD FREE
PARTICULATES	• Pass waste gases through sprays of water or filters to remove particles. • Electrically charged precipitators can be used to attract dust particles.	
SULPHUR DIOXIDE	• Use low-sulphur fuels. • 'Scrub' the gas from the power station chimneys by spraying the pollutant gases.	SULPHUR FREE
CARBON MONOXIDE	• Use of more efficient engines which completely burn the fuel. • Catalytic converters to convert carbon monoxide to CO_2	
OXIDES OF NITROGEN	• Use a catalytic converter in which nitrogen monoxide combines with carbon monoxide to produce nitrogen and carbon dioxide.	

GLOBAL WARMING

- The 10 warmest years of the 20th century have all occurred within the last 15 years, with 1998 the warmest.
- Snow cover and ice in the Arctic have all decreased.
- Sea level has risen by between 12 and 24cm since 1900.
- Global rainfall over land has risen by more than 1%.
  These powerful pieces of evidence encourage scientists to believe that global warming is occurring and will continue to do so.

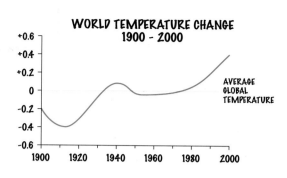

WORLD TEMPERATURE CHANGE
1900 - 2000

AVERAGE GLOBAL TEMPERATURE

GREENHOUSE EFFECT

- The Sun is the major source of ENERGY for the Earth.
- It heats up the Earth's surface which in return ...
  ... radiates heat energy back into space.
  Gases in the atmosphere, including CARBON DIOXIDE ...
  ... trap some of the heat energy that the Earth's surface radiates out.
  Increasing levels of carbon dioxide mean that more heat is trapped.
  A similar thing happens in a greenhouse where heat energy is trapped ...
  ... inside the greenhouse because of its glass panels.
  This is why the trapping of heat energy by the Earth's atmosphere ...
  ... is known as the GREENHOUSE EFFECT and results in GLOBAL WARMING.

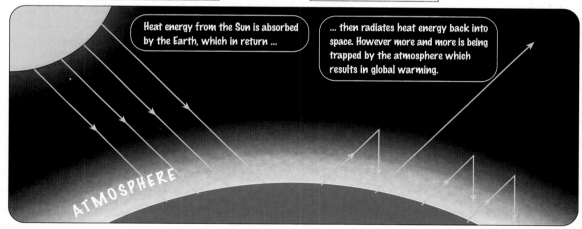

Heat energy from the Sun is absorbed by the Earth, which in return ...

... then radiates heat energy back into space. However more and more is being trapped by the atmosphere which results in global warming.

ATMOSPHERE

Unless action is taken there will be two particular consequences for life on Earth.

1. SEA LEVELS will continue to rise because the polar ice caps are melting.
2. CLIMATE will become UNPREDICTABLE with some places becoming wetter or drier than at present.

This will disrupt the growth of food crops and the ecosystems of plants and animals.

UPSETTING THE BALANCE

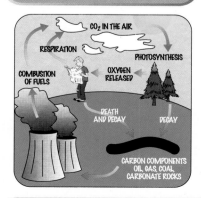

CO₂ IN THE AIR

RESPIRATION

PHOTOSYNTHESIS

COMBUSTION OF FUELS

OXYGEN RELEASED

DEATH AND DECAY

DECAY

CARBON COMPONENTS OIL, GAS, COAL, CARBONATE ROCKS

Until relatively recently the balance between adding and removing carbon dioxide from the atmosphere worked perfectly. The levels of carbon dioxide and oxygen were maintained by photosynthesis and respiration. However, two important factors have upset the balance ...

1. Excessive burning of fossil fuels is increasing the amount of carbon dioxide in the atmosphere.

2. Deforestation of large areas of the Earth's surface means the amount of photosynthesis is reduced so less carbon dioxide is removed from the atmosphere.

KEYWORDS

Match the keywords from this unit to their definitions ...

ACID RAIN	Commonly known as limestone, it contains calcium, carbon and oxygen
SULPHUR DIOXIDE	Organic material in soils. It can include the roots of living plants and the remains of dead plants
OXIDES OF NITROGEN	Compounds containing hydrogen and carbon only
POLLUTION	Colourless gas produced by the action of sunlight on oxygen and pollutants.
AIR QUALITY	Has a pH of less than 7 and damages the natural environment on which it falls
HYDROCARBONS	Compounds produced by burning fossil fuels. They contain oxygen and nitrogen
CARBON MONOXIDE	Solids, such as rock particles, which have been deposited by rivers and streams
OZONE	The levels of pollution in the gases which we breathe
pH	Toxic gas containing carbon and oxygen
CALCIUM CARBONATE	Harmful gas produced by volcanic activity and burning fossil fuels
SEDIMENT	Increase in average temperatures due to changes in the levels of atmospheric gases
VEGETATION	Scale indicating the acidity or alkalinity of a substance
GREENHOUSE EFFECT	Man-made substances which cause harmful changes to the natural environment
GLOBAL WARMING	The build up of heat in the Earth's atmosphere due to the presence of certain gases

SMOG

Read this passage and then answer the questions below.

Smog is an urban phenomenon ie. it is a problem in towns and cities where there is a lot of industrial activity and heavy traffic. In London in 1952, four thousand people were killed by smog and its effects. In 1956, yet more people died because of the smog, and this eventually led to the Clean Air Act which gave Local Authorities the power to create 'smokeless zones'. People were encouraged to burn smokeless fuel or to start using natural gas and electricity for their heating. This has undoubtedly improved the quality of the air which we breathe, but the problems have not been completely erased. Air pollution caused the deaths of over 150 people in December 1991 and caused severe breathing difficulties for many people in 1995. A newer problem is photochemical smog, a harmful combination of smoke and fog produced when sunlight reacts with hydrocarbons and oxides of nitrogen.

1. Why did smog become a worse problem in the 20th Century than in previous centuries?

2. Who might have opposed the Clean Air Act?

3. Does the Clean Air Act mean that we don't pollute the atmosphere when we heat our homes?

4. What effect do you think the Clean Air Act had on the coal industry?

5. Do you think the quality of air will improve or worsen in the 21st Century? Explain your answer.

6. What measures could we take to reduce the occurrence of photochemical smog?

GLOBAL WARMING

The main source of energy for the Earth is the .... The earth absorbs .... energy from the .... and in return it radiates .... energy back into space. Unfortunately this energy is trapped by gases in the .... , which include .... This is known as the .... effect. A similar thing happens in a .... where heat energy is trapped by the glass panels. The .... effect is the cause of .... warming.

There is evidence that this is occurring: sea levels have .... ; there has been a .... in snow cover and ice in the Arctic; global rainfall over land has .... If the trend continues then sea levels will continue to ...... and the .... will become unpredictable, leading to disruption in the growth of .... crops and the ecosystems of .... and ....

Photosynthesis and .... are two factors that have until recently, kept the levels of .... and oxygen in the atmosphere fairly constant. The balance has now changed due to too much burning of .... fuels which has .... the level of .... Also, the cutting down of forests has reduced the amount of .... taking place, with less .... being removed from the atmosphere.

AIR POLLUTANTS

The table below gives the emission rates (in millions of tonnes per year) for the main pollutants in the UK.

POLLUTANT	CARBON MONOXIDE	SULPHUR DIOXIDE	HYDROCARBONS	PARTICULATES	OXIDES OF NITROGEN
EMISSION RATE (millions of tonnes/year)	95	31	30	25	19

1. Show these results on the pie chart opposite.

2. What are the main sources of the following pollutants:

   i) carbon monoxide?

   ....

   ii) sulphur dioxide?

   ....

   iii) hydrocarbons?

   ....

3. Name one other pollutant of our atmosphere which isn't in the table above.

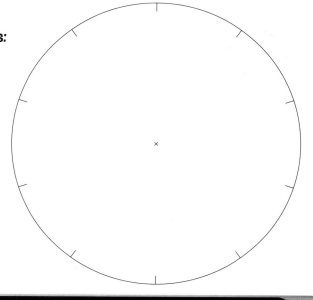

A group of students decided to investigate the effect of acid rain on the germination of cress seeds. Cress seeds were arranged on cotton wool, placed in a petri dish and watered with a very dilute solution of sulphuric acid.

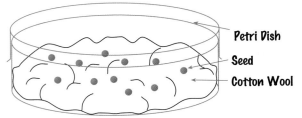

The investigation was repeated using another four petri dishes where the strength of the acid sprinkled onto the seeds was gradually increased, compared to the standard strength of the first acid used, ie. the acid in the second petri dish was twice (2x) as strong, the acid in the third petri dish was three (3x) as strong etc. The experiment was carried out three times for each concentration of acid.

1. Which variables need to be controlled in order to make this a fair test?

....

....

2 Which variable is difficult to control and may affect the results?

....

3. If you were carrying out this investigation, how would you control this variable?

....

....

4. The results obtained are as follows.

STRENGTH OF ACID	x1	x2	x3	x4	x5
NUMBER OF SEEDS GERMINATING	20	12	10	7	1
	20	13	12	9	1
	17	14	14	18	4
AVERAGE No. OF SEEDS GERMINATING					

One of the results in the table is wrong. Ignore this result and complete the table by working out the average number of seeds germinating.

5. i) On the graph paper provided plot points to show the results.

   ii) Draw a line of best fit.

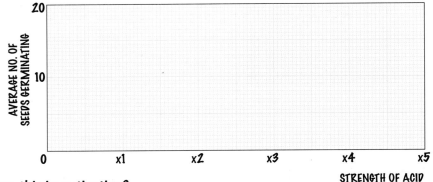

6. What conclusions can you draw from this investigation?

....

....

7. What was the advantage in repeating the investigation three times for each concentration of acid?

....

8. Suggest a reason why the students may have obtained a wrong result.

....

BURNING FUELS

A FUEL is a substance that releases ENERGY, as HEAT and LIGHT, when it is burned.

The three fuels above, although they look physically different, all contain HYDROGEN and CARBON. They can only burn if OXYGEN (from the air) is available. The products formed when they burn depend on the amount of oxygen available. For example, if we take METHANE ie. natural gas and there is plenty of oxygen available ...

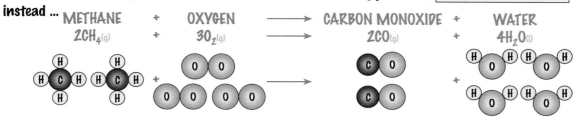

| METHANE | + | OXYGEN | ⟶ | CARBON DIOXIDE | + | WATER |
| $CH_{4(g)}$ | + | $2O_{2(g)}$ | ⟶ | $CO_{2(g)}$ | + | $2H_2O_{(l)}$ |

... then there would be COMPLETE COMBUSTION

Sometimes, the fuel burns without sufficient oxygen eg. in a room with poor ventilation, then INCOMPLETE COMBUSTION takes place and instead of carbon dioxide being produced, CARBON MONOXIDE is produced instead ...

| METHANE | + | OXYGEN | ⟶ | CARBON MONOXIDE | + | WATER |
| $2CH_{4(g)}$ | + | $3O_{2(g)}$ | ⟶ | $2CO_{(g)}$ | + | $4H_2O_{(l)}$ |

... and if there is very little oxygen available, CARBON is produced instead ...

| METHANE | + | OXYGEN | ⟶ | CARBON | + | WATER |
| $CH_{4(g)}$ | + | $O_{2(g)}$ | ⟶ | $C_{(s)}$ | + | $2H_2O_{(l)}$ |

Although these fuels do produce useful amounts of energy when they burn, the GASES they produce are POLLUTANTS ...

... CARBON DIOXIDE, contributes to the GREENHOUSE EFFECT which results in GLOBAL WARMING.

... CARBON MONOXIDE, a poisonous gas, combines with haemoglobin in the red blood cells more readily than oxygen.

HYDROGEN AS A FUEL

If you put a lighted splint into a test tube of HYDROGEN it 'POPS' because an explosive reaction takes place between the HYDROGEN and the OXYGEN (in the air) to form WATER.

POP!!!

| HYDROGEN | + | OXYGEN | ⟶ | WATER |
| $2H_{2(g)}$ | + | $O_{2(g)}$ | ⟶ | $2H_2O_{(l)}$ |

This method of producing energy has been used to power rockets for a long time. In this case the rocket carries its own supply of liquid hydrogen and liquid oxygen.

Another important development is the hydrogen powered engine which hopefully one day will replace the internal combustion engine. The great advantage of this development is that NO carbon dioxide or carbon monoxide is produced.

ENERGY FROM DISPLACEMENT REACTIONS

If a piece of metal is brought into contact with a solution of a compound of a metal which is lower in the REACTIVITY SERIES a DISPLACEMENT reaction will occur. (See Page 42)
The less reactive metal will be 'pushed out' of solution to become an element, while the more reactive one will go into solution as a compound.

MAGNESIUM RIBBON — COPPER SULPHATE SOLUTION — COPPER COATING — MAGNESIUM SULPHATE

This reaction releases energy to the surroundings causing a temperature rise. The bigger the difference in reactivity of the two metals, the more energy is released.

MAGNESIUM + COPPER SULPHATE ⟶ MAGNESIUM SULPHATE + COPPER + ENERGY
$Mg_{(s)}$ + $CuSO_{4(aq)}$ ⟶ $MgSO_{4(aq)}$ + $Cu_{(s)}$ + ENERGY

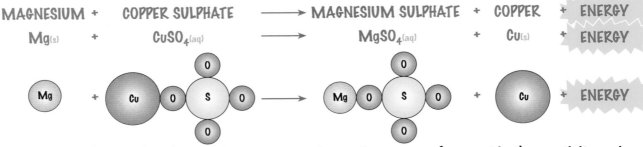

This reaction releases a lot of energy because magnesium and copper are far apart in the reactivity series. The following reaction would produce far less energy because the metals are closer together...

ZINC + COPPER SULPHATE ⟶ ZINC SULPHATE + COPPER + ENERGY
$Zn_{(s)}$ + $CuSO_{4(aq)}$ ⟶ $ZnSO_{4(aq)}$ + $Cu_{(s)}$ + ENERGY

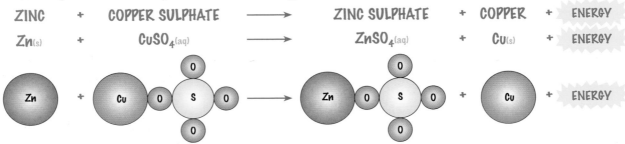

ELECTRICAL ENERGY FROM DIFFERENCES IN REACTIVITY

Differences in the reactivity of two metals can be used to generate electricity rather than heat. Zinc and Copper rods connected to a voltmeter by copper wire can be used as a simple VOLTAIC CELL ...

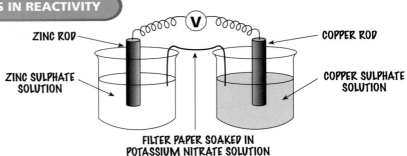

ZINC ROD — COPPER ROD — ZINC SULPHATE SOLUTION — COPPER SULPHATE SOLUTION — FILTER PAPER SOAKED IN POTASSIUM NITRATE SOLUTION

The 'bridge' of filter paper allows the circuit to be completed, and the bigger the difference in reactivity between the two metals, the bigger the voltage.

A SPECTACULAR DISPLACEMENT REACTION

In the thermit reaction, aluminium powder displaces iron from iron oxide. The iron is produced in molten form due to the heat released by the reaction.

MAGNESIUM RIBBON 'FUSE' — ALUMINIUM POWDER AND IRON OXIDE — SMALL PLUG OF IRON REMAINS

ALUMINIUM + IRON OXIDE ⟶ IRON + ALUMINIUM OXIDE
$2Al_{(s)}$ + $Fe_2O_{3(s)}$ ⟶ $2Fe_{(s)}$ + $Al_2O_{3(s)}$

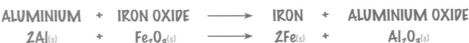

CHEMICAL SUBSTANCES

Everything around you is some sort of chemical, in one sense. You are surrounded by SUBSTANCES ...

... as solids (like your desk), as liquids (that you drink) and as gases (that you breathe) etc.

Some are NATURAL but many have been made in a factory. These are said to be SYNTHETIC.

Many of them have been DEVELOPED for a particular purpose. Here are some examples.

SHAMPOOS
- to remove dirt!

PLASTICS
- to make hundreds of things

PAINTS
- to decorate and protect

ANAESTHETICS
- for painless operations

EXPLOSIVES
- for war and peace
(eg. mining.)

ALLOYS
- for particular jobs

DYES
- for numerous purposes

... and the list goes on
.... and on ...

CHEMICALS FOR CONSUMPTION

Of course, anything that is going to be sold to the public has to be tested to make sure it is SAFE as well as doing the job it is supposed to. (Nowadays people are beginning to economise on their use of resources, recycle materials if possible, and reduce pollution.)

For instance, food colourings need to be tested to see if they are poisonous or have ill effects on the people who eat them. Sometimes the tests are carried out using animals first, then people.

 All drugs have to be extensively tested before they can be marketed or prescribed for people. They have to be checked for side effects as well as doing the job they are intended for. Sometimes <u>years</u> of testing are needed.

ENERGY FROM CHEMICALS

There are now millions of chemical compounds known. As well as making NEW SUBSTANCES chemical reactions can also be used to provide ENERGY. This can be done by simply BURNING FUELS but there are lots of other ways to get energy from chemicals.

eg.

ENERGY from CELLS
is changed to LIGHT

SELF-HEATING can of food
uses REACTIONS in its base

ENERGY from CELLS
changes to MOTION

FISHERMAN'S hand
warmer releases heat from
a reaction

CHEMICAL REACTIONS

These are also important in all living things. Both plants and animals use reactions to release energy from foodstuffs during respiration to allow them to move, grow etc. All living things need to make NEW MOLECULES for GROWTH, REPAIR, REPLACEMENT etc. For example, PLANTS make glucose during PHOTOSYNTHESIS, animals make proteins to build up MUSCLES.

REACTANTS AND PRODUCTS

The 'REACTANTS' is the name given to the substances we start with at the beginning of a chemical reaction.
The 'PRODUCTS' is the name given to the substances which are formed during a chemical reaction.
An important point about this is ...

> THE TOTAL MASS OF REACTANTS IS ALWAYS THE SAME AS THE TOTAL MASS OF THE PRODUCTS BECAUSE ALL THE ATOMS ARE STILL THERE AT THE END.

EXAMPLES OF CONSERVATION OF MASS IN REACTIONS

For each of the following reactions, count up the numbers of different types of atom in the reactants and compare this to the numbers of the products ...

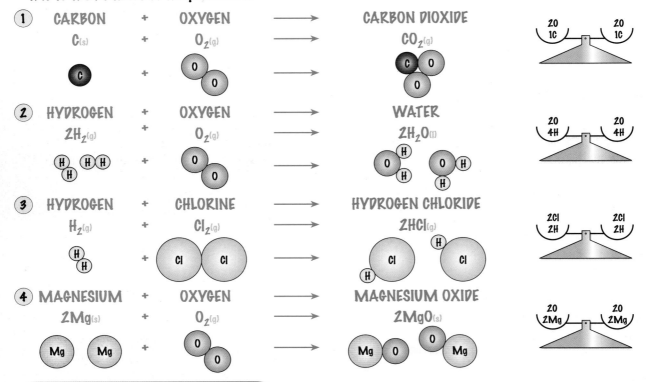

① CARBON + OXYGEN ⟶ CARBON DIOXIDE
$C_{(s)}$ + $O_{2(g)}$ ⟶ $CO_{2(g)}$

2O 1C | 2O 1C

② HYDROGEN + OXYGEN ⟶ WATER
$2H_{2(g)}$ + $O_{2(g)}$ ⟶ $2H_2O_{(l)}$

2O 4H | 2O 4H

③ HYDROGEN + CHLORINE ⟶ HYDROGEN CHLORIDE
$H_{2(g)}$ + $Cl_{2(g)}$ ⟶ $2HCl_{(g)}$

2Cl 2H | 2Cl 2H

④ MAGNESIUM + OXYGEN ⟶ MAGNESIUM OXIDE
$2Mg_{(s)}$ + $O_{2(g)}$ ⟶ $2MgO_{(s)}$

2O 2Mg | 2O 2Mg

ESCAPING MASS DURING BURNING

If you burn Magnesium in a crucible after first weighing it you will notice that the white ash of magnesium oxide weighs less than the magnesium you started with!!

This used to puzzle scientists in centuries gone by until they realised that some of the mass was escaping with the 'smoke' from the burning substance. If a substance is burned in an enclosed container then the final mass of the oxide will be greater than the mass of the original substance. This increase is due to the addition of oxygen.

BURNING HYDROCARBONS

HYDROCARBONS are compounds which consist of hydrogen and carbon. When these substances burn in air they form two products, ...

METHANE + OXYGEN ⟶ CARBON DIOXIDE + WATER
$CH_{4(g)}$ + $2O_{2(g)}$ ⟶ $CO_{2(g)}$ + $2H_2O_{(l)}$

The CO_2 and H_2O escape into the air resulting in an <u>apparent</u> loss of mass.

KEYWORDS

Match the keywords from this unit to their definitions ...

FUEL	A simple cell in which the difference in reactivity of two metals is used to generate electricity
CARBON MONOXIDE	When the metal in a metal compound, is replaced by a more reactive metal
DISPLACEMENT	Substances which react together in a chemical reaction
REACTIVITY SERIES	A dangerous product of incomplete combustion
VOLTAIC CELL	A substance in which oxygen is combined with one other element
SYNTHETIC	A principle which states that the mass of the reactants in a chemical reaction is equal to the mass of the products
REACTANTS	A substance that releases energy as heat or light when burned
PRODUCTS	Man-made as opposed to naturally occurring
CONSERVATION OF MASS	A rank order of metals in order of their reactivity
HYDROCARBON	Substances which are produced as a result of a chemical reaction
OXIDE	An interaction between atoms and/or molecules which leads to the production of new substances
CHEMICAL REACTION	A substance made up entirely of hydrogen and carbon atoms

FUEL CELLS

Read this passage and then answer the questions below.

Primitive fuel cells were first designed more than 200 years ago but they are still expensive to produce today. Consequently, this fact, added to their relative bulkiness means that they are still not yet commercially viable. Nevertheless they are often used in space where they are operated at their most efficient using pure Hydrogen and Oxygen to provide electrical energy and water, which is their only waste product - although it is absolutely pure and can be drunk.

There are currently experiments in operation which use fuel cells in vehicles, for example a fuel cell taxi has been used in London. Fuel cell buses have been running for over two years in America and some companies have been working on a range of vehicles, including cars, which they hope to make available in the not too distance future.

If oil prices continue to rise then the race to perfect fuel cell technology will accelerate. A firm move in this 'direction' would be bad for the economics of the world's oil producers but excellent for the environmental future of our planet.

1. What do you think would contribute most to the bulkiness of fuel cells?

2. What particular advantage is there in using fuel cells in outer space?

3. What do you think is the main reason for fuel cell technology not having taken over the automobile industry?

4. Why will a significant rise in oil prices cause a greater use of fuel technology?

5. Why will this be of benefit to our planet?

6. Write down both word and symbol equations for the reaction of hydrogen and oxygen in a fuel cell.

PRODUCING ENERGY

When .... burn they release .... in the form of heat. Many of the fuels we use contain the elements .... and .... As a result they are called .... A simple example would be .... whose formula is CH_4. When there's plenty of oxygen present, methane burns to produce .... and .... However if there is insufficient .... then methane undergoes .... combustion to produce .... and .... This is important when burning gas fires in poorly ventilated rooms, since .... is a poisonous gas which may cause death. Even when burnt completely, the .... given off contributes towards .... Energy produced by .... is very clean. The differences in .... between two metals can be used to produce .... or electricity. The greatest voltage is produced by metals which are far apart in the ....

BURNING MAGNESIUM

Pupils performed a very carefully controlled experiment to investigate the mass of magnesium oxide produced by burning a known mass of magnesium. They obtained the following results ...

MASS OF MAGNESIUM (g)	0	2	4	6	8	10	12
MASS OF MAGNESIUM OXIDE (g)	0	3.3	6.7	10	13.3	16.7	20

1. Plot a graph to show the data.

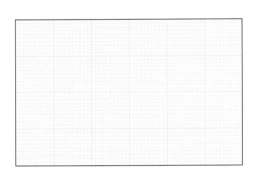

2. How much magnesium oxide would 5g of magnesium produce?

....

3. What mass of magnesium would produce 15g of magnesium oxide?

....

4. What mass of oxygen would need to react with magnesium to produce 8.3g of magnesium oxide?

....

5. What mass of oxygen would need to react with 6g of magnesium to produce the mass of magnesium oxide shown in the data.

Wasim, Grace and James used the equipment shown in the diagram to investigate the voltage produced by combinations of different metals.

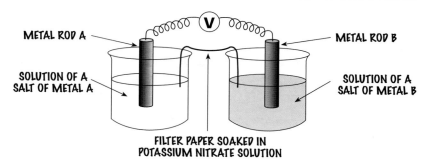

METAL ROD A
METAL ROD B
SOLUTION OF A SALT OF METAL A
SOLUTION OF A SALT OF METAL B
FILTER PAPER SOAKED IN POTASSIUM NITRATE SOLUTION

Their results were as follows

ROD A	ALWAYS MAGNESIUM					
ROD B	ZINC	'X'	'Y'	LEAD	COPPER	SILVER
VOLTAGE PRODUCED (V)	1.6	1.8	2.0	2.3	2.8	3.2

1. Plot these as a bar chart on the graph paper below.

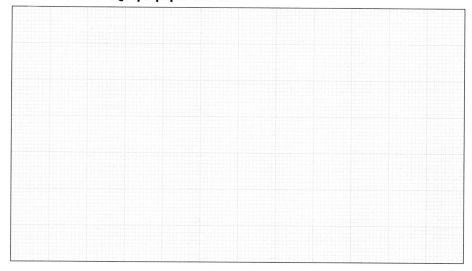

2. The students weren't told the identity of metals 'X' and 'Y'.
    Use your knowledge of reactivity to suggest what they might be.

    Metal 'X' ....

    Metal 'Y' ....

3. Suggest a salt which could be used as solution A.

    ....

4. Suggest a salt which could be used as solution B when the metal rod being used was copper.

    ....

5. Which variables would the students have had to control to make this a fair test?

    ....

    ....

6. When they repeated the investigation using a zinc and copper rod they produced a voltage of 1.2volts.
    Explain this using data from the original investigation.

    ....

    ....

FORMS OF ENERGY

ENERGY exists in many forms. Here are the most common ones. You will already be familiar with most of them.

LIGHT

Energy given out by some hot objects (and some cold ones). Light energy travels from the sun by radiation.

SOUND

Energy created by any vibrating object.

ELECTRICAL

Our most convenient form of energy.

HEAT

Energy which an object has due to the kinetic (movement) energy of its particles. Heat energy travels from the sun by radiation.

CHEMICAL

Energy contained in food, fuel or a battery

KINETIC

The energy an object has because it is moving.

POTENTIAL

A form of stored energy which an object has by virtue of its position.

STORING ENERGY

Energy can be STORED so that the stored energy can be used at a more convenient time.

① A STRETCHED or COMPRESSED SPRING ...
... is a store of **POTENTIAL ENERGY** which ...
... can be transferred into **KINETIC ENERGY.**

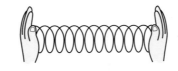

② A CELL or a BATTERY is a store of **CHEMICAL ENERGY** which can be transferred ...
... into **ELECTRICAL ENERGY** in a complete circuit.

1.5V   6V   12V

All cells and batteries have a certain VOLTAGE which is measured in VOLTS. The GREATER THE VOLTAGE, THE GREATER THE AMOUNT OF ELECTRICAL ENERGY THAT CAN BE TRANSFERRED into other forms of energy by components or devices in a complete electrical circuit.

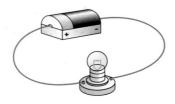

TWO CELLS WILL TRANSFER A GREATER AMOUNT OF ELECTRICAL ENERGY AND THE BULB LIGHTS UP MORE BRIGHTLY.

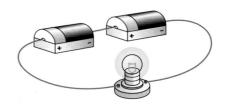

ELECTRICAL ENERGY AND VOLTAGE

- An electrical circuit transfers electrical energy from a cell, battery or power supply to components in the circuit.
- Provided the circuit is complete an electric current flows through the components and <u>electrical energy is transferred into other forms of energy.</u>

ELECTRICAL ENERGY IS TRANSFERRED INTO LIGHT ENERGY

ELECTRICAL ENERGY IS TRANSFERRED INTO HEAT ENERGY

- A simple model to illustrate this is the 'up-and-down' ski-lift, where the chairs are the current which flows around the circuit, the ski-lift motor is the battery providing the voltage, and the skiers are the energy climbing on at the motor-house and getting off at suitable places (components) around the ski-lift circuit ...

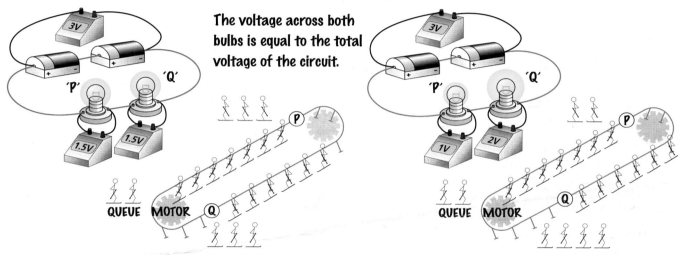

The voltage across both bulbs is equal to the total voltage of the circuit.

- In the first example, the two bulbs are identical and the same amount of energy is transferred at each bulb. This makes them equally bright.
- In the second example, the bulbs have different resistances and therefore different voltages across them. Bulb Q transfers energy at a faster rate and is therefore brighter.
- Our ski-lift model shows the same number of skiers getting off at P and Q in the first example but twice as many getting off at Q compared to P in the second example.
- Notice that the current (the chairs) doesn't get used up - it just keeps going round and round.

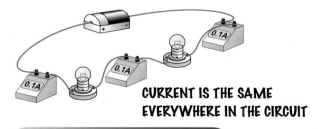

CURRENT IS THE SAME EVERYWHERE IN THE CIRCUIT

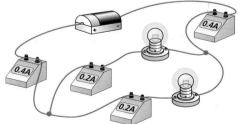

EVEN IF THE CURRENT SPLITS UP, THE TOTAL OF THE 'SPLIT' CURRENT IS EQUAL TO THE CURRENT IN THE MAIN CIRCUIT.

DANGERS OF HIGH VOLTAGES

Really high voltages can transfer huge amounts of energy. For example, lightning occurs where there is a large build up of potential difference between the clouds and the earth. This P.D. (or voltage) can cause the lightning to 'jump across' the air to the ground. This can also happen if you get too close to High Voltage power lines. You don't have to actually touch them.

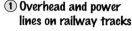

① Overhead and power lines on railway tracks

② Lightning

GENERATION OF ELECTRICITY

Electricity is generated in a POWER STATION using a range of ENERGY RESOURCES ...

... FOSSIL FUELS

These are burnt to release their energy.
However, once they have been used ...
... they CANNOT BE USED AGAIN.
This is why the FOSSIL FUELS are called ...
... NON-RENEWABLE ENERGY RESOURCES.
Although they produce plenty of energy ...
... they are environmentally damaging.

... RENEWABLES

Unlike the non-renewables ...
... once they have been used, ...
... they CAN BE USED AGAIN ...
... because they are continually being replaced.
Not much energy is produced by these ...
... but at least they are environmentally friendly.

COAL

... NUCLEAR FUEL
Another NON-RENEWABLE ...
... although it is not a fossil fuel ...
... and is not burnt ...
to release energy.
Again, plenty of energy
is produced ...
... but at a cost to the environment.

WIND

NATURAL GAS

MINERAL OIL

WAVES

RUNNING WATER

- Although, each of the above resources are different the one thing they have in common ...
  ... is that each one can be used to cause movement in a TURBINE ...
  ... which drives a **GENERATOR,** where **KINETIC ENERGY** is TRANSFERRED into **ELECTRICAL ENERGY.**

A bicycle DYNAMO is a very simple generator where the movement ...
... of the bicycle wheel causes a magnet and its surrounding ...
... magnetic field to rotate inside the dynamo.
This rotating magnetic field is 'cut' by the coil of wire which ...
... causes electrical energy to be produced in it.
The faster the dynamo rotates the more electrical energy is produced.

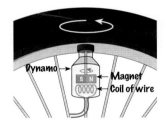

CONSUMPTION OF ELECTRICITY

Electrical appliances can be connected to the 'mains supply', via sockets, ...
... from which ELECTRIC CURRENT flows through components in the appliances.
These components then transfer **ELECTRICAL ENERGY** into OTHER FORMS OF ENERGY which are of use to us.
All appliances have a **POWER RATING** , measured in watts, W, which tells us ...
... how much ENERGY is TRANSFERRED by that appliance EVERY SECOND.
Different appliances have different power ratings.
Those with higher power ratings transfer energy at a faster rate and are consequently more expensive to use.

A COMPUTER MONITOR
transfers energy at a rate of
200 watts (joules per second).

A DRILL
transfers energy at a rate of
500 watts (joules per second).

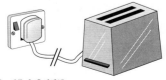

A TOASTER
transfers energy at a rate of
1000 watts (joules per second).

When energy is transferred from ONE FORM TO ANOTHER only part of the INPUT ENERGY is usefully transferred how and where it is wanted as OUTPUT ENERGY. We always end up with some of the energy being transferred in a non-useful way and therefore WASTED.

Energy is always CONSERVED, which means that the TOTAL INPUT ENERGY in JOULES (J) is always equal to the TOTAL OUTPUT ENERGY, even though some of this is wasted energy.

| DEVICE | ENERGY TRANSFER |

① TUNGSTEN FILAMENT LIGHT BULB

ELECTRICAL ENERGY, 100 J

HEAT ENERGY, 80J
(wasted)

LIGHT ENERGY, 20J
(useful)

② LOW ENERGY LIGHT BULB

ELECTRICAL ENERGY, 100J

HEAT ENERGY, 20J
(wasted)

LIGHT ENERGY, 80J
(useful)

③ ELECTRIC KETTLE

ELECTRICAL ENERGY, 100J

SOUND ENERGY, 5J
(wasted)

HEAT ENERGY, 5J
(wasted in element)

HEAT ENERGY, 90J
(useful)

④ ELECTRIC DRILL

ELECTRICAL ENERGY, 100J

SOUND ENERGY, 20J
(wasted)

HEAT ENERGY, 20J
(wasted)

KINETIC ENERGY, 60J
(useful)

⑤ FOSSIL FUEL POWER STATION

CHEMICAL ENERGY, 100J

HEAT ENERGY, 15J
(wasted in burning fuel)

HEAT ENERGY, 50J
(wasted in turbine)

HEAT ENERGY, 5J
(wasted in generator)

ELECTRICAL ENERGY, 30J
(useful)

KEYWORDS

Match the keywords from this unit to their definitions ...

LIGHT	A fuel or a battery is a store of this energy
SOUND	Non-renewable energy resources that are burnt to release their energy
ELECTRICAL	In a complete circuit this flows through components and is not used up
HEAT	A device where kinetic energy is converted into electrical energy
CHEMICAL	A vibrating object creates this form of energy
KINETIC	An instrument used for measuring voltage
POTENTIAL	Energy resources that are continually being replaced
ELECTRIC CURRENT	Energy given out by some hot objects and possibly some cold ones
VOLTMETER	A form of stored energy eg. in a stretched spring
FOSSIL FUELS	Objects have this due to the kinetic energy of their particles
NUCLEAR FUEL	The rate at which an electrical appliance transfers energy
RENEWABLES	A non-renewable but it is not a fossil fuel
GENERATOR	A form of energy transferred around circuits and transformed in components
POWER RATING	The form of energy possessed by a moving object

DEVELOPMENT OF THE ELECTRIC MOTOR AND THE GENERATOR

Read this passage and then answer the questions below.

In 1820 the Danish scientist, Hans Christian Oersted found that if he brought a wire, which was carrying an electric current near to a compass, the needle of the compass was deflected. He realised that this was only possible if a magnetic field was formed around the wire while it carried an electric current. In effect Oersted had made the first electromagnet. A year later Michael Faraday carried out an experiment where he suspended a wire between the north pole of one magnet and the south pole of another magnet. When he passed an electric current through the wire, the wire was deflected. He realised that this movement of the wire was a result of the magnetic field which had formed around the current-carrying wire, interacting with the magnetic field between the two poles of the magnets. Known as the 'motor effect' it consequently led to the development of the electric motor.

It took a further 10 years for Faraday to produce the reverse effect, in other words using a magnetic field and movement to produce an electric current. He found that if a wire 'cuts' through a magnetic field an electric current is produced in the wire providing the wire moves and also that it is part of a complete circuit. This is known as electromagnetic induction and is the principle behind the development of the generator.

1. Describe in your own words the discovery made by Oersted.
2. What would have happened to the compass needle if Oersted had brought a wire near to it which wasn't carrying an electric current? Explain your answer.
3. Explain why the wire deflected in Faraday's experiment.
4. What would happen if the current was passed through the wire in the opposite direction?
5. a) In electromagnetic induction, explain why a current is only produced if
   i) the wire moves and
   ii) the wire is part of a complete circuit.
   b) What energy transfer takes place in electromagnetic induction?

TRANSFER OF ENERGY

Energy is often transferred from one form to another, so that it can be of use to us eg. an electric kettle transfers

.... energy into .... energy; a microphone transfers .... energy into ....

energy. Energy can also be stored so that it can be used later eg. a battery is a store of .... energy

which can be later transferred as .... energy; a compressed spring is a store of .... energy

which can be later transferred as .... energy.

Cells and batteries have a certain voltage which is measured in .... The greater the voltage, the greater

the amount of .... energy that can be transferred. Voltage is measured using a voltmeter connected

.... the components, unlike electric current which is measured using an .... connected in

.... with the components.

Energy sources that cannot be used again are called .... There are two types:

fuels and .... fuel. Sources that can be used again are called .... All of these sources can

be used to drive a generator where .... energy is transferred into .... energy, which is

then distributed all over the country.

Electrical appliances can then transfer this .... energy into other forms of energy. Different appliances

have different power .... which tell us how much energy the appliance transfers every ....

When an energy transfer takes place, energy is conserved with the total .... energy always equal to

the total .... energy.

ENERGY AND APPLIANCES

1. Complete the table below which gives the energy input per second,
the useful energy output per second and the wasted energy output per second for five appliances.

APPLIANCE	ENERGY INPUT/SEC (J/s)	USEFUL ENERGY OUTPUT/SEC (J/s)	WASTED ENERGY OUTPUT/SEC (J/s)
A	100	60	
B	300		180
C		130	70
D	50		26
E	500	200	

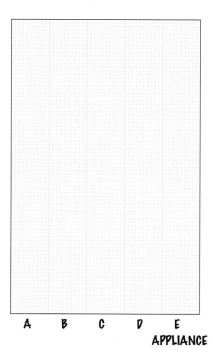

A   B   C   D   E
APPLIANCE

2. Which appliance wastes the least energy, for every 100J of

   energy input per second? ....

3. Which appliance produces the smallest percentage of useful energy?

   ....

4. On the axes given draw a bar graph to show the useful percentage
   energy output for each appliance.

Chloe is investigating how the voltage across one component in a series circuit depends on the number of components in the circuit. She is given **5** identical components, a **3** volt battery and wires.

1. Which other piece of equipment does she need to complete her investigation? Explain your choice.

....

2. What variables must Chloe keep the same in order to make this a fair test?

....

....

3. She firstly connected one component in series and then two, three, four and finally all five.
   Each time she measured the voltage across one component in the circuit. Her results are as follows:

NO. OF COMPONENTS	1	2	3	4	5
VOLTAGE ACROSS ONE COMPONENT	3	1.5	1.0	0.7	0.6

   i) On the graph paper provided plot points to show her results.

   ii) Draw a curve on your graph that passes through all the points.

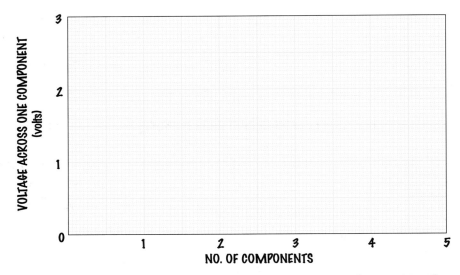

4. Explain why the voltage reading across one component decreases as the number of components in the circuit increases.

....

....

5. What else decreases in a series circuit as the number of components in the circuit increases?
   Explain fully how Chloe could show this.

....

....

6. With three components in the circuit, Chloe measured the voltage across a second component: it was 1 volt.
   What is the voltage across the third component in this circuit? Explain your answer.

....

....

WHAT IS GRAVITY?

GRAVITY is an ATTRACTIVE FORCE which affects everything. Any two objects which have MASS each exert an equal and opposite attractive force on each other. This force depends on the masses of the objects and their distance apart. On Earth, gravity acts towards its centre and if we were to drop an object, eg. a ball, anywhere on Earth it would be pulled 'downwards' towards its centre.

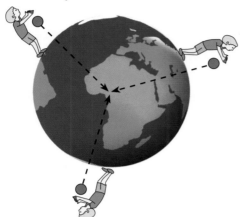

It should be remembered that as the Earth's gravity is pulling the ball downwards, the ball is also pulling the Earth upwards!

However, since the mass of the Earth is massive compared to the ball, the pull force on the Earth due to the ball is next to nothing and so the ball falls downwards rather than the Earth 'falling upwards'. Sir Isaac Newton was the first person to formulate a theory to explain gravity from the falling down of apples from trees to the motion of the planets around the Sun.

MASS AND WEIGHT

The MASS of an object is the amount of matter that it contains. On Earth an object of MASS 1 KILOGRAM (kg) experiences a downward pull force, or has a WEIGHT of 10 NEWTONS (N). ie. the weight of an object on Earth in newtons (N) is always 10 TIMES BIGGER than its mass in kilograms.

However ...

... on the MOON or a DIFFERENT PLANET the SAME OBJECT would have the SAME MASS but a different WEIGHT! For example if we take an object with a mass of 1kg ...

- On the MOON its weight would be about 1.6N this is ONE SIXTH its value on Earth. This is because the Moon has a smaller mass compared to Earth and consequently it exerts a smaller gravitational pull on the object.

- On JUPITER its weight would be about 26N which is over two and a half times its value on Earth. This is because it has a bigger mass compared to Earth.

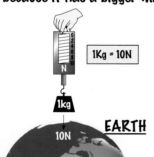

1Kg = 10N

EARTH

10N

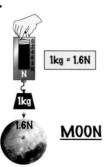

1kg = 1.6N

1.6N

MOON

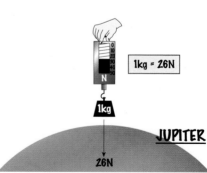

1kg = 26N

26N

JUPITER

On the Moon a person's muscles including their heart muscle, wouldn't have to work as hard.

To overcome this the person would have to exercise to stop their muscles becoming weaker. This problem is even worse in the weightlessness of space, and astronauts have to be careful if they are in space for a long time.

... On EARTH

Mass (kg)	Weight (N)
1	10
2	20
5	50
10	100

... On the MOON

Mass (kg)	Weight (N)
1	1.6
2	3.2
5	8
10	16

... On JUPITER

Mass (kg)	Weight (N)
1	26
2	52
5	130
10	260

A rocket can only 'TAKE OFF' if it can overcome the GRAVITATIONAL ATTRACTION of the Earth.
The THRUST FORCE produced by the rocket must be GREATER than the WEIGHT of the rocket in order
for it to accelerate for sufficient time to reach a speed high enough to 'escape' the gravitational
attraction of the Earth. This is known as the Escape Velocity.

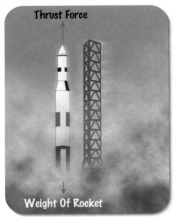

Rockets carry their own supply of fuel. The enormous heat generated
by burning this fuel creates gases which are forced out through a nozzle
at the rear of the rocket to produce a downward force. Since forces
always act in pairs an equal and upwards force is exerted on the rocket.
This is the THRUST FORCE.

As the rocket gets further and further away from the Earth a SMALLER THRUST FORCE is now needed
to produce the SAME ACCELERATION because the WEIGHT OF THE ROCKET has DECREASED.
This is due to a <u>combination</u> of two things ...

1. GRAVITATIONAL ATTRACTION OF THE EARTH DECREASING.

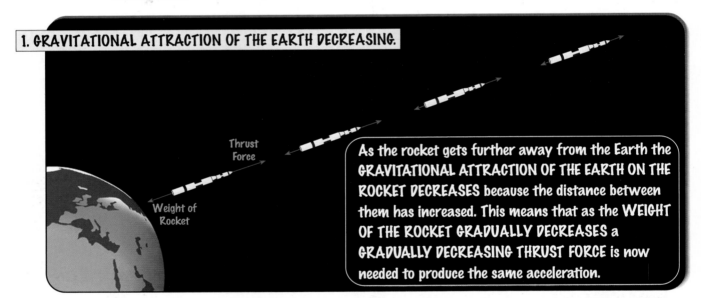

As the rocket gets further away from the Earth the
GRAVITATIONAL ATTRACTION OF THE EARTH ON THE
ROCKET DECREASES because the distance between
them has increased. This means that as the WEIGHT
OF THE ROCKET GRADUALLY DECREASES a
GRADUALLY DECREASING THRUST FORCE is now
needed to produce the same acceleration.

2. MASS OF THE ROCKET DECREASING.

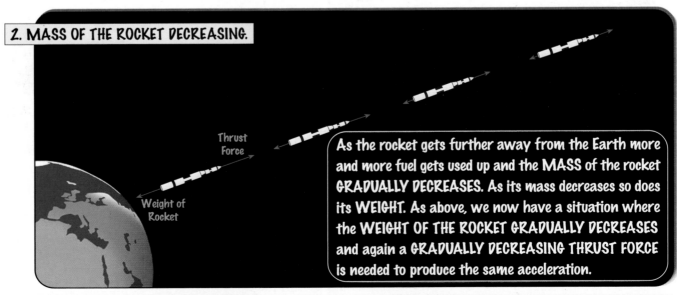

As the rocket gets further away from the Earth more
and more fuel gets used up and the MASS of the rocket
GRADUALLY DECREASES. As its mass decreases so does
its WEIGHT. As above, we now have a situation where
the WEIGHT OF THE ROCKET GRADUALLY DECREASES
and again a GRADUALLY DECREASING THRUST FORCE
is needed to produce the same acceleration.

A SATELLITE is an OBJECT which is in orbit around a LARGER OBJECT.
The smaller object stays in its orbit because the larger object exerts an INWARD PULL FORCE on it.

If you swing a rubber ball attached to a piece of string in a horizontal
circle then the inward force that keeps the ball moving in its circular
orbit is provided by the tension force in the string.
As you swing the ball you can feel this tension which is keeping the
ball moving in its orbit.

However, if the string was to suddenly snap then the tension force
which keeps the ball moving in a circular orbit would immediately
disappear causing the ball to fly off!

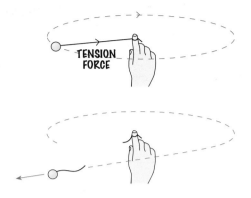

NATURAL SATELLITES OF THE SUN

For over 2000 years there have been a variety of different ideas concerning the arrangement of the
SOLAR SYSTEM.

- PYTHAGORAS (500 BC) and PTOLEMY (120 AD) both proposed that the Earth was at the centre of the solar
  system with the Sun in orbit around it. This was called the GEOCENTRIC MODEL.
- ARISTARCHUS (300 BC) and COPERNICUS (1540 AD) both proposed that the Sun was the centre,
  with the Earth in orbit around it. This was called the HELIOCENTRIC MODEL.
- GALILEO (1610 AD) discovered four moons orbiting Jupiter, which was evidence for the heliocentric model.
- ISAAC NEWTON (1640 AD) using his theory of gravity, proved that the EARTH and the OTHER PLANETS
  are NATURAL SATELLITES of the SUN.

Unlike the ball above, the planets are not kept in their orbit by a piece of string but by the VERY LARGE
GRAVITATIONAL FORCE of the Sun. This gravitational force, like the tension in the string, acts inwards
towards the Sun.

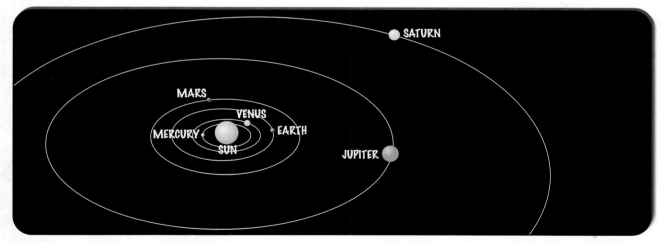

If the gravitational force of the Sun was to suddenly disappear then the Earth and other planets would go flying
off into space (in a straight line!).

THE NATURAL SATELLITE OF THE EARTH

Just as the planets are natural satellites of the Sun, the MOON is a
NATURAL SATELLITE of the EARTH. Here, the INWARD GRAVITATIONAL
FORCE of the Earth keeps the Moon in its orbit. The Sun also influences
the Moon's orbit but to a much lesser extent because the Earth is much
closer to the Moon than the Sun.

There are many ARTIFICIAL SATELLITES in orbit AROUND THE EARTH. Each one has been put in orbit by us to perform a particular task ...

1. MONITORING THE WEATHER

These collect information about the atmosphere including the movement of clouds so that weather forecasts can be made. The satellite has a LOW POLAR ORBIT ie. it passes continuously over the north and south poles. They orbit and scan the Earth several times every day.

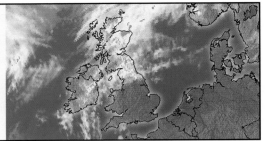

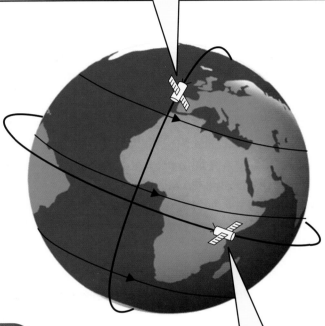

2. COMMUNICATION

These link up different countries often in different continents so that radio, TV broadcasts and telephone calls can be sent from one country to another. The satellite has an orbit passing over the equator which takes 24 hours to complete. This means that it always stays at the same point above the equator, ie. it has a GEOSTATIONARY ORBIT .

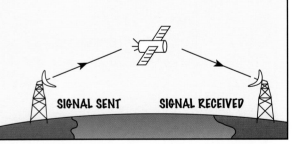

SIGNAL SENT   SIGNAL RECEIVED

3. EXPLORATION OF THE SOLAR SYSTEM

These are in orbit ABOVE THE EARTH'S ATMOSPHERE. They have telescopes and the solar system and beyond can be observed without any interference from the atmosphere, clouds and weather storms. The most famous is the HUBBLE SPACE TELESCOPE which was launched in 1990 to make observations of the Universe and it has even taken pictures of galaxies that cannot be detected here on Earth!

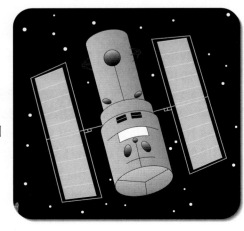

KEYWORDS

Match the keywords from this unit to their definitions ...

GRAVITY	The unit used for measuring mass
MASS	Rockets can only accelerate if this is greater than their weight
KILOGRAMS	Orbit of a satellite used to monitor the weather
WEIGHT	The rate by which something increases in speed
NEWTONS	A man-made object which orbits the Earth
THRUST FORCE	Downward pull force on an object due to gravity
ACCELERATION	Orbit of a satellite used to link up different continents
NATURAL SATELLITE	An attractive force that exists between objects with mass
ARTIFICIAL SATELLITE	A rocky or gaseous body which orbits a planet or the Sun
LOW POLAR ORBIT	The amount of matter that an object contains
GEOSTATIONARY ORBIT	The unit used for measuring weight

APOLLO 13

Read this passage and then answer the questions below.

On Saturday, 11th April 1970, Apollo 13 was launched into space with three crew members: Lovell, Haise and Swigert. Their aim was to land on the moon. However, 56 hours into their flight, one of their oxygen tanks blew up and the other one subsequently failed. Although they had sufficient back-up oxygen for their return to Earth, the explosion meant that water and power were in short supply, and they would no longer be able to land on the Moon. Mission control decided that the best plan was to carry on and orbit the moon before returning to Earth. This would take nearly four days, during which time the three men would be supported by the Lunar Module which was designed only to support two men for half that time. The shortage of water, electricity and light caused the main problems, their water intake was reduced by four-fifths and upon their return all three men were dehydrated. Their electricity and light usage was also cut down to four-fifths of normal consumption, which meant that there was no heating within the spacecraft. Condensation formed on the interior walls and on re-entry it 'rained' in the craft. The other major problem was the removal of carbon dioxide. As the men were breathing, they breathed out carbon dioxide; the levels became dangerously high as the standard system of 'cleansing' the air was not operational. Eventually, Lovell was able to make a device which helped to purify the air. They finally returned safely to Earth, landing in the Pacific Ocean on Friday, 17th April 1970.

1. Explain in terms of the forces acting how Apollo 13 was launched into space.
2. When they first encountered problems why didn't they turn around and return to Earth?
3. Why would they need heating in space?
4. In what way did the gravitational pull of the moon help them?
5. Explain why condensation formed on the inside walls of their craft.
6. In what way did the gravitational pull of the Earth help them?

EFFECT OF GRAVITY

The .... of an object is the amount of matter that it contains. It is measured in ....

On Earth an object experiences a downwards force or has .... which is, numerically,

.... times bigger than its .... On the Moon however the .... of

an object is about one sixth its value on the .... although its .... doesn't change.

Rockets can only take off if they can overcome the .... attraction of the Earth. In order for a

rocket to accelerate its .... force must be greater than its .... As the rocket gets

further away from the Earth a smaller .... force is needed to produce the same acceleration

because the .... of the rocket has decreased.

A satellite is an object which is in .... around a much .... object. It stays in its

orbit because the .... object exerts an inward pull .... on it. The Earth is a

.... satellite of the Sun, and the Moon is a .... satellite of the Earth.

Satellites that have been put into orbit around the Earth are known as .... satellites. Those that

monitor the weather have a low .... orbit, while those used for communication have a

.... orbit, which takes .... hours to complete.

WEIGHT AND MASS

The graph below shows the relationship between the weight of an object and its mass, for the Earth and either
the Moon or Jupiter.

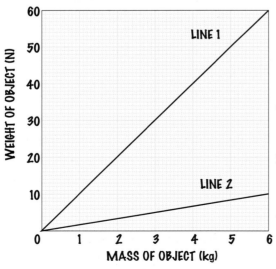

1. Which line represents the relationship for an object on Earth?
   Explain your answer. ....
   ....
   ....

2. If the mass of an object is 3.5 kg, use the graph to calculate
   its weight on Earth ....

3. If the weight of an object on Earth is 600N, what is its mass?
   ....

4. The other line represents the relationship for an object on the
   Moon or Jupiter. Explain which one it is likely to be.
   ....
   ....
   ....

A pupil was asked to investigate whether there was a relationship between the tension force in a string attached to a small object which is swung around in a horizontal circular orbit and its radius of orbit. All other possible variables were kept constant. The pupil was given the following data.

TENSION FORCE (N)	5.9	3.1	2.0	1.6	1.2	0.9
RADIUS OF ORBIT (m)	0.2	0.4	0.6	0.8	1.0	1.2

1. a) On the graph paper provided, plot points to show the data.

   b) Draw a curve on your graph paper which passes through all the points.

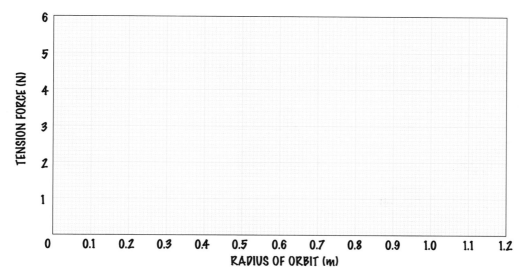

2. What relationship is there between the tension force and radius of orbit?

....

3. Use the graph to estimate the tension force if radius of orbit is:

   a) 0.5m ....   b) 0.9m ....

4. The pupil was told that there was a relationship between the tension force and speed of rotation. All other possible variables were kept constant. The pupil was given the following data.

TENSION FORCE (N)	1.1	2.2	3.9	6.3	9.0	12.3
SPEED OF ROTATION (m/s)	1.0	1.5	2.0	2.5	3.0	3.5

In what way is the relationship between tension force and speed of rotation different to the relationship between tension force and radius of orbit?

....

....

5. a) Which other variable, apart from radius of orbit and speed, do you think would affect the

   tension force? ....

   b) What sort of relationship will there be between the tension force and this variable?

....

MEASURING SPEED

One way of describing the movement of an object is by measuring its **SPEED.**

● An athlete running at a steady speed of 6 metres per second (6m/s) ...

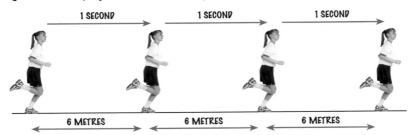

... would travel a **DISTANCE of 6 METRES EVERY 1 SECOND.**

● A motorcyclist travelling at a steady speed of **50 miles per hour (50mph)** ...

... would travel a **DISTANCE of 50 MILES EVERY 1 HOUR.**

In order to work out the **SPEED** of any moving object we need to know two things.

❶ THE DISTANCE IT TRAVELS and ...   ❷ THE TIME IT TAKES TO TRAVEL THAT DISTANCE.

We can then use the relationship that links distance, time and speed.

$$\text{SPEED (m/s)} = \frac{\text{DISTANCE TRAVELLED (m)}}{\text{TIME TAKEN (s)}}$$

This relationship can be put into a formula triangle which makes things a lot easier when the relationship needs to be rearranged.

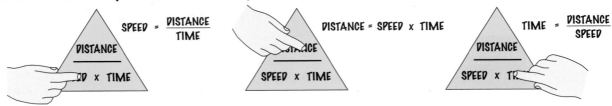

$$\text{SPEED} = \frac{\text{DISTANCE}}{\text{TIME}} \qquad \text{DISTANCE} = \text{SPEED} \times \text{TIME} \qquad \text{TIME} = \frac{\text{DISTANCE}}{\text{SPEED}}$$

EXAMPLES

❶ Calculate the speed of an athlete who runs 200 metres in 25 seconds.

Using our relationship: $\text{SPEED} = \dfrac{\text{DISTANCE TRAVELLED}}{\text{TIME TAKEN}} = \dfrac{200\text{m}}{25\text{s}} = 8\ \text{m/s.}$

❷ A car on the motorway travels at an average speed of 100 km/h for 150 minutes. How far does the car travel?

Time given is in **MINUTES**, and we need it in **HOURS** because the **SPEED** is in kilometres per **HOUR** ...

... 150 minutes = $\frac{150}{60}$ hours = **2.5 hours**

Using our relationship (rearranged using the formula triangle).   **DISTANCE = SPEED × TIME = 100 km/h × 2.5h = 250 km**

The movement of any object depends on the forces that are acting on it.
If these forces acting are the same size but in opposite directions then the forces acting are **BALANCED.**
Otherwise an **UNBALANCED** force acts. In the following we have ignored any forces that act on the object
in an upwards or downwards direction as they play no part in the movement.

HOW BALANCED FORCES AFFECT MOVEMENT

There are two possibilities.

① A **STATIONARY** OBJECT will REMAIN STATIONARY ...

... if the forces acting are **BALANCED.**   ... or if there is NO FORCES ACTING AT ALL.

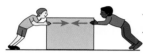

The two pupils both push with the same force. The box remains stationary.

There are no forces acting on the car and so it remains stationary.

② A MOVING OBJECT will CARRY ON AT THE SAME STEADY SPEED if the forces acting are **BALANCED.**

FRICTIONAL FORCE   THRUST FORCE

If the thrust force of the engine is equal to the frictional force then the moving car will carry on at the same speed.

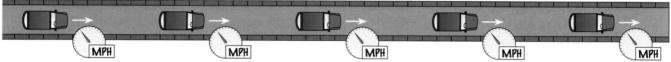

In deep outer space a moving object will carry on moving at the same steady speed even if there are no forces
acting on it. On Earth this is impossible and even if friction can be reduced to zero there will always be
AIR RESISTANCE (see next page) which opposes the movement.

HOW UNBALANCED FORCES AFFECT MOVEMENT

An **UNBALANCED FORCE** acting on an object will cause it to SPEED UP (ACCELERATE) or SLOW DOWN (DECELERATE).

THRUST FORCE

If the car is stationary and the driver presses the accelerator then the thrust force of the engine causes an unbalanced force to act. The car will now move and speed up. However, as soon as the car moves the force of friction comes into play.

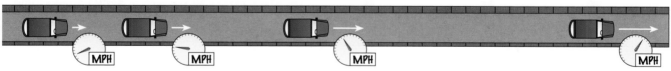

FRICTIONAL FORCE

The driver now takes his foot off the accelerator and he presses the brake pedal. The frictional force between the brake pads and the wheels causes an unbalanced force to act and the car will now slow down.

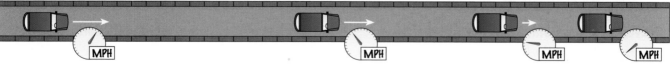

EFFECT OF MASS ON MOVEMENT

The **LARGER THE MASS** of an object that an UNBALANCED FORCE acts on ...
... the smaller the **ACCELERATION** or **DECELERATION** of the object.

If the boy exerts the same push force on a trolley of BIGGER MASS ...
... then the acceleration he achieves will be smaller.

AIR RESISTANCE AND WATER RESISTANCE

AIR RESISTANCE ...

... is the FORCE that acts against a moving object as it passes through air.

AIR RESISTANCE

VEHICLE IS MOVING IN THIS DIRECTION

WATER RESISTANCE ...

... is the FORCE that acts against a moving object as it passes through water.

WATER RESISTANCE

BOAT IS MOVING IN THIS DIRECTION

One way that the vehicle and the boat can increase their speed without having to increase the thrust force of their engines is to reduce the amount of resistance acting against them.

This can be done by STREAMLINING the object so that it 'cuts through' the air or water more easily.

AIR RESISTANCE

WATER RESISTANCE

Vehicles are now designed to reduce the amount of air resistance acting on them. This helps to save money in the amount of fuel they use.

Many marine animals are streamlined to reduce the amount of water resistance acting on them. This is useful for both predator and prey.

EFFECT OF SPEED ON AIR RESISTANCE

The FASTER AN OBJECT MOVES through air or water the GREATER THE RESISTANCE which acts against it. You can experience this effect if first you walk, then jog and then run.

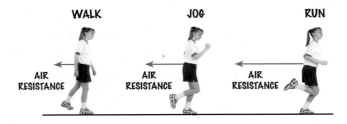

WALK JOG RUN

AIR RESISTANCE AIR RESISTANCE AIR RESISTANCE

As you run faster, you need to use up more ENERGY in order to overcome the INCREASING FORCE OF AIR RESISTANCE which is acting against you.

Vehicles also have the same problem, because the faster they move the greater their FUEL CONSUMPTION. Here are some typical fuel consumption figures for a car:

travelling at a constant speed of **56mph** this car will do approximately **45 miles to the gallon.**

travelling at a constant speed of **70mph** the same car will do approximately **33 miles to the gallon.**

PARTICLE MODEL AND AIR RESISTANCE

As an object passes through air it collides with AIR PARTICLES. This causes AIR RESISTANCE. The faster the object moves the more collisions there are, compared to a slower moving object.
This results in an increased 'air' resistance.

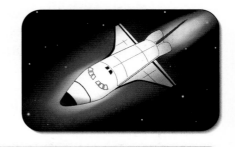

Falling objects experience TWO FORCES.

① The DOWNWARD FORCE OF $\boxed{\text{WEIGHT, W}}$ (↓) which always stays the same.

② The UPWARD FORCE OF $\boxed{\text{AIR RESISTANCE, R}}$ or DRAG (↑).

A typical falling object is a skydiver who jumps out of an aeroplane.
The speed of his descent can be considered as two separate parts ...

... BEFORE THE PARACHUTE IS OPENED

① As the skydiver jumps out of the plane the only force acting on him is $\boxed{\text{WEIGHT, W.}}$
The skydiver experiences $\boxed{\text{AIR RESISTANCE, R}}$ as soon as he falls.

② As he falls unbalanced forces act because **W** is bigger than **R** and the speed of
the skydiver increases. However as his speed increases so does the air resistance
acting on him.

③ Eventually **R** increases until it is equal to **W**. The forces acting on
the skydiver are now balanced and he falls at a steady speed.

④

... AFTER THE PARACHUTE IS OPENED

⑤ When the parachute is opened unbalanced forces
act again because the upward force of **R** is now
greatly increased and is bigger than **W**. This
decreases his speed and as his speed decreases
so does **R**.

⑥ Eventually **R** decreases until it
is equal to **W**. The forces acting
are once again balanced and
for the second time he falls at
a steady speed, slower than
before though, ...

⑦

⑧ ... and eventually
lands safely.

Graph — SPEED OF SKYDIVER vs TIME:
④ STEADY SPEED
③
② SPEED INCREASES
①
⑤ SPEED DECREASES
⑥
⑦ **⑧** STEADY SPEED
BEFORE | AFTER
TIME

KEYWORDS

Match the keywords from this unit to their definitions ...

SPEED	Force that acts against a falling object
BALANCED FORCES	The distance travelled by an object divided by the time taken remains constant
UNBALANCED FORCES	The rate of decrease in the speed of an object
STATIONARY	When the forces acting on an object are equal and opposite
STEADY SPEED	Smooth shape which reduces the amount of air or water resistance
ACCELERATION	The distance travelled by an object divided by the time taken
DECELERATION	Downward force that acts on an object
AIR RESISTANCE	The rate of increase in the speed of an object
WATER RESISTANCE	Describes an object which isn't moving
STREAMLINED	A visual display which records changes in motion
WEIGHT	When the forces acting on an object are not equal and opposite
SPEED-TIME GRAPH	Force that acts against a moving object as it passes through water

THE EARLY DEVELOPMENT OF THE HOVERCRAFT

Read this passage and then answer the questions below.

A Swedish inventor, Emmanual Swedenborg designed the first hovercraft in the early eighteenth century. It was a one person air-cushioned craft which was lifted above the surface of the water as air was forced beneath the hull. However the design was totally impractical because it replied on the efforts of a single person generating the movement of the air - an impossible task!

150 years later, Sir John Thornycroft also tried to reduce the amount of water resistance experienced by boats and ships, using the same principles; as there were no engines available at that time he experienced similar difficulties and he was unable to provide enough movement of air with which to support the craft.

Finally, in the 1950's, Christopher Cockerell used a different approach. He placed nozzles aimed inwards around the underneath of the perimeter of the craft. As air was forced out through them it formed a continuous air cushion, which was trapped beneath the craft and thus supported the weight of it. Some of this air cushion was expelled via the rear of the craft which propelled it forwards. This idea was known as the air-flow system and was the key to further progress.

1. In Swedenborg's design, why would it have been impossible for one person to generate sufficient air movement?
2. Why is it desirable to reduce the amount of water resistance experienced by boats and ships?
3. In Christopher Cockerell's design what effect would there be if the nozzles were all aimed outwards?
4. Cockerell's hovercraft was propelled forwards due to the expulsion of air from the rear of the craft. Explain why this would propel the craft forward.
5. Hovercrafts experience less water resistance than other boats and ships. Explain why.
6. With its engines turned on, what would be the main forces acting on a stationary hovercraft?

FORCES IN ACTION

The speed of a moving object is the .... travelled by the object divided by the .... it takes to travel it. Speed is commonly measured in metres per .... , kilometres per .... or .... per hour.

The forces acting on an object are balanced if they are the same .... but in opposite .... Balanced forces acting on an object will cause a non-moving object to remain .... while a moving object will carry on moving at the same steady .... Unbalanced forces acting on an object will, however, cause it to .... or ....

Air .... and .... resistance are two forces which act against a moving object as it passes through air and water respectively. The amount of .... acting can be reduced by .... the object, although it does get greater the faster the object moves. This is why the .... consumption of a vehicle increases if it travels faster.

All falling objects experience two forces: .... and .... The motion of a falling object can be visually displayed by means of a .... graph.

SPEED-TIME GRAPH

The table below gives the speed of a car, from rest, at 10 second intervals for the first 100 seconds of its motion.

SPEED (m/s)	0	4	8	12	12	12	12	15	18	21	24
TIME (s)	0	10	20	30	40	50	60	70	80	90	100

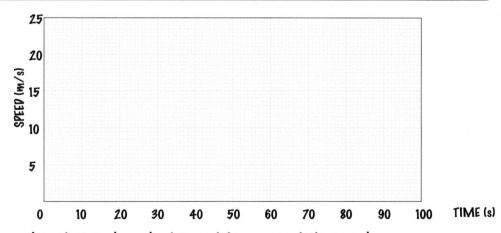

1. On the axes given, plot points to show the data and draw a speed-time graph.

2. In which period of time were the forces acting on the car balanced? Explain your answer.

   ....

   ....

3. In which period of time were the forces acting on the car unbalanced by the greatest amount? Explain your answer. ....

Freya is asked to investigate whether there is a relationship between the speed of a car and the resistive forces which act on it.

1. Give two factors that should be kept constant in order to carry out a fair test.

   i) ....

   ii) ....

2. She is given the following data:

RESISTIVE FORCE ACTING (N)	0	90	300	760	1460
SPEED OF CAR (m/s)	0	10	20	30	40

Draw a graph to show the data.

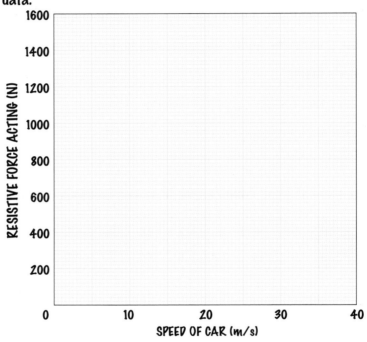

3. What conclusion could Freya form from the data given?

   ....

   ....

4. Using the data above to support your answer, explain why the fuel consumption of a car increases as the speed of the car increases.

   ....

   ....

5. Describe two things which could be done to a car to increase its maximum speed.

   ....

   ....

   ....

PRESSURE, FORCE AND AREA

PRESSURE is exerted whenever a FORCE is APPLIED OVER AN AREA.
The amount of pressure exerted depends on:

1 THE SIZE OF THE FORCE.

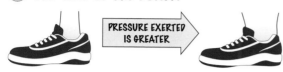

An INCREASED FORCE (ie. a heavier person) ...
... results in a GREATER PRESSURE BEING EXERTED ...
... on the ground, providing ...
... AREA IN CONTACT STAYS THE SAME.

The relationship between pressure, force and area is:

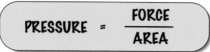

PRESSURE = $\dfrac{\text{FORCE}}{\text{AREA}}$

This relationship can be put into a formula triangle which makes things a lot easier when the relationship needs to be rearranged.

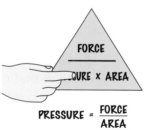

PRESSURE = $\dfrac{\text{FORCE}}{\text{AREA}}$

2 THE SIZE OF THE AREA.

A DECREASED AREA (ie. stiletto heels) ...
... results in a GREATER PRESSURE BEING EXERTED ...
... on the ground, providing ...
... FORCE APPLIED STAYS THE SAME.

Pressure is measured in ...
- ... Newtons per millimetre squared (N/mm^2)
- ... Newtons per centimetre squared (N/cm^2)
- ... Newtons per metre squared (N/m^2)

FORCE = PRESSURE x AREA

AREA = $\dfrac{\text{FORCE}}{\text{PRESSURE}}$

EXAMPLES

1 A woman weighing 600N stands on one foot only. The area of foot in contact with the ground is 120cm². Calculate the pressure she exerts on the ground.

Using our relationship: PRESSURE = $\dfrac{\text{FORCE}}{\text{AREA}}$ = $\dfrac{600N}{120cm^2}$ = $5N/cm^2$

2 Another woman stands on one foot only, with the same area in contact with the ground. She exerts a pressure of 5.5N/cm² on the ground. Calculate the weight of the woman.

Using our relationship: FORCE = PRESSURE x AREA = 5.5N/cm² x 120cm² = 660N

PRACTICAL APPLICATIONS OF PRESSURE

If the AREA is LARGE this results in a SMALL PRESSURE being exerted ...

FOUNDATIONS OF BUILDINGS TO PREVENT BUILDING SINKING.

SNOW SKIS TO PREVENT SINKING INTO THE SNOW.

If the AREA is SMALL this results in a LARGE PRESSURE being exerted ...

ICE SKATES CAUSE THE ICE TO MELT AT POINT OF CONTACT, REDUCING FRICTION.

SHARP KNIFE BLADES TO MAKE IT EASIER TO 'CUT' THROUGH FOOD.

PRESSURE IN GASES

If you inflate a bicycle tyre with air, many millions of tiny gas particles enter the tyre. Once inside, these gas particles constantly hit the inside surface of the tyre because they are moving around very quickly and in all directions. This constant hitting of the inside surface creates gas pressure and the more air that is pumped into the tyre the greater the pressure since there are more collisions.

A spray aerosol (eg. an air fresher) uses the same principle ...

... but this time a gas under pressure inside the can ...

... acts as a propellant for the liquid inside it ...

... when the aerosol button is pressed.

Even when 'empty' you should never throw an aerosol can on a fire as the gas particles inside would gain energy causing them to move around much faster. This increase in GAS PRESSURE could cause the can to explode!

PRESSURE IN LIQUIDS

Liquids can be put under pressure. However, since the particles in a liquid are packed closely together, unlike those in gas, liquids are INCOMPRESSIBLE (cannot be squashed), for this reason pressure can be transmitted through the liquid, by the particles. An example of this in action is the hydraulic car jack, a force multiplier.

① A force exerted on the master piston puts the liquid in the jack under pressure.

③ Since the area of the slave piston is greater than that of the master piston then the force exerted on the slave piston is now multiplied in the ratio of their areas

② This pressure is transmitted from the master piston through the liquid to the slave piston.

 EXAMPLE

The hydraulic jack above has a force of 500N applied to the master piston of area 5cm². The slave piston has an area of 50cm². What is the force exerted on the slave piston?

RATIO of AREA OF SLAVE PISTON to AREA OF MASTER PISTON is 50cm² :5cm² = 10:1

The FORCE EXERTED on the SLAVE PISTON is increased in COMPARISON ...

... to the FORCE EXERTED on the MASTER PISTON ...

... BY THE SAME RATIO.

Therefore, the force exerted on slave piston = 10 x 500N = 5000N

PRESSURE AND DEPTH OF FLUID

The pressure in a FLUID (a gas or a liquid) depends on ...

① ... the WEIGHT of fluid above the point being considered.

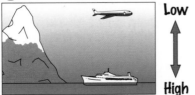

Low ↕ High

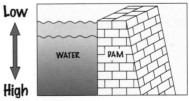

Low ↕ High

Aeroplanes are 'pressurised' to have ...

... a similar pressure as on ground level ...

... because atmospheric pressure decreases with height.

The thickness of a dam increases towards the base ...

... because the pressure of a liquid ...

... increases with depth.

② ... the DENSITY of the fluid.

The GREATER the density of the fluid, the GREATER the PRESSURE at ANY POINT compared to a less dense fluid.

HOW LEVERS WORK

A LEVER is a very simple machine. All levers have a PIVOT and its position relative to the EFFORT FORCE (ie. the force put in) and the LOAD FORCE (ie. the force got out) determines how easily the lever enables us to carry out a task.

A crowbar is a very common lever and here it is being used to move a large boulder.
As you can see the position of the pivot is very important as it determines the EFFORT FORCE needed to overcome the LOAD FORCE of the boulder. If the pivot is ...

... CLOSER TO THE EFFORT FORCE THAN THE LOAD FORCE then ...

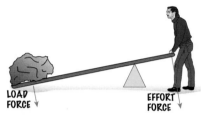

... the effort force needs to be BIGGER than the load force in order to overcome it.

... THE SAME DISTANCE FROM THE EFFORT FORCE AND LOAD FORCE then ...

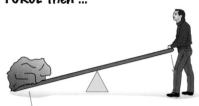

... the effort force needs to be SAME as the load force in order to overcome it.

... CLOSER TO THE LOAD FORCE THAN THE EFFORT FORCE then ...

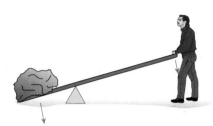

... the effort force needs to be LESS than the load force in order to overcome it. The lever now acts as a FORCE MULTIPLIER.

OTHER COMMON EXAMPLES OF LEVERS IN ACTION

All of these are examples of levers acting as FORCE MULTIPLIERS.

① **REMOVING THE LID FROM A TIN OF PAINT.**

② **USING A PAIR OF SCISSORS**

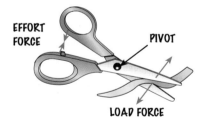

③ **USING A SPANNER**

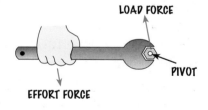

LEVERS IN THE BODY

BONES that make up LIMBS eg. the arm and leg, behave as levers where their movement is controlled by the CONTRACTION OF MUSCLES. In the arm the BICEPS MUSCLE and the TRICEPS MUSCLE are called ANTAGONISTIC MUSCLES because they act to oppose each other's movement. The lower part of the arm can behave as a lever to lift a load, because the BICEPS acts as the effort and the ELBOW the pivot.

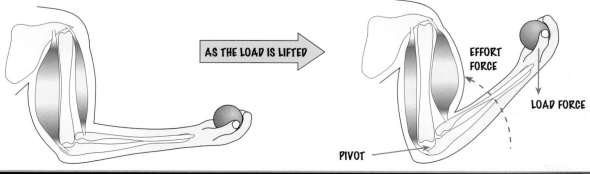

AS THE LOAD IS LIFTED

MOMENTS

Forces can be used to TURN OBJECTS ABOUT A PIVOT.
A spanner is being used to unscrew a wheel nut.
The spanner exerts a MOMENT or TURNING FORCE
on the nut given by the relationship ...

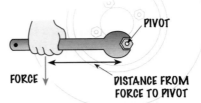

FORCE

DISTANCE FROM
FORCE TO PIVOT

PIVOT

MOMENT = FORCE x DISTANCE TO PIVOT

Moment is measured in ...
- ... Newton metre, Nm.
- ... Newton centimetre, Ncm.

If the MOMENT is BIG ENOUGH it will unscrew the nut, if it isn't, there are TWO ways of increasing it.

① INCREASE THE DISTANCE FROM FORCE TO PIVOT ...
   ... use a spanner with a longer handle.

② INCREASE THE FORCE APPLIED ...
   ... push harder.

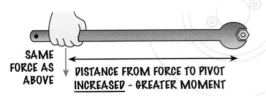

SAME
FORCE AS
ABOVE

DISTANCE FROM FORCE TO PIVOT
INCREASED - GREATER MOMENT

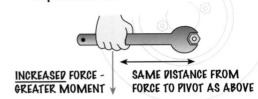

INCREASED FORCE -
GREATER MOMENT

SAME DISTANCE FROM
FORCE TO PIVOT AS ABOVE

PRINCIPLE OF MOMENTS

The see-saw below has two children on it, one either side.

THE BOY EXERTS
AN ANTI-CLOCKWISE
MOMENT ABOUT
THE PIVOT.

THE GIRL EXERTS
A CLOCKWISE
MOMENT ABOUT
THE PIVOT.

PIVOT

If the MOMENT exerted by the boy is EQUAL to the MOMENT exerted by the girl then the see-saw is BALANCED.
This is known as the PRINCIPLE OF MOMENTS . When balanced ...

TOTAL CLOCKWISE MOMENT = TOTAL ANTI-CLOCKWISE MOMENT

EXAMPLE

The boy in the diagram above weighs 500N and he is 2m from the pivot.
Where must a girl, who weighs 400N, sit in order for the see-saw to be balanced?

When balanced:

TOTAL CLOCKWISE MOMENT = TOTAL ANTI-CLOCKWISE MOMENT

400N x DISTANCE TO PIVOT = 500N x 2m

$$\text{DISTANCE TO PIVOT} = \frac{500N \times 2m}{400N}$$

$$= 2.5m$$

TOPPLING OVER

Sometimes the moment exerted by a force can make an object topple over.
If you stand with your heels against a wall ...
... and try to pick up an object 50cm away.

Cranes have a 'counterbalance' weight
to stop them from toppling over.

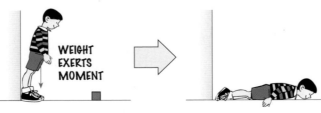

WEIGHT
EXERTS
MOMENT

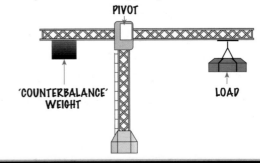

PIVOT

'COUNTERBALANCE'
WEIGHT

LOAD

The moment exerted by your weight will make you ...
... lose your balance and you'll topple over. (Try it).

KEYWORDS

Match the keywords from this unit to their definitions ...

PRESSURE	A gas or a liquid
INCOMPRESSIBLE	A turning force exerted about a pivot
GAS PRESSURE	A simple machine made up of a pivoted rod
FLUID	The force opposing the effort in a lever
LEVER	A pair of these produce turning effects at some skeleton joints
PIVOT	Exerted when a force is applied over an area
EFFORT	The point about which a lever moves
LOAD	In a balanced system, the clockwise and anti-clockwise moments are equal
FORCE MULTIPLIER	Created when gas particles constantly hit the inside surface of their container
ANTAGONISTIC MUSCLES	Describes a substance whose volume cannot be reduced
MOMENT	A machine that enables a small effort force to overcome a larger load force
PRINCIPLE OF MOMENTS	The force attempting to move the load in a lever

THE BENDS

Read this passage and then answer the questions below.

The bends (also known as decompression sickness or Caisson disease) originally got its name because sufferers are often unable to straighten their joints. It is a condition which can affect anyone subjected to abnormal pressures, namely deep-sea divers, pilots of unpressurised aircraft and Caisson workers (construction workers using underwater cabins).

At normal atmospheric pressure gases are present in the body, but they are usually in solution. When external pressure increases they begin to saturate the tissues. The main gas responsible for this is nitrogen, because carbon dioxide is continuously exhaled as a waste product and oxygen is used by the body cells with the result that the level of nitrogen builds up in the body. When the pressure on the body returns to its usual level, the excess nitrogen is expelled. However, if it is not allowed to occur slowly, bubbles will form in the tissues. It is these bubbles which can cause a wide variety of symptoms within 15 minutes to 12 hours of returning to normal atmospheric pressure. The symptoms can be as mild as itching, rashes or tiredness to painful limbs, paralysis and unconsciousness.

1. What is the origin of the term 'the bends'?
2. Why are deep-sea divers subjected to abnormal pressures?
3. Why are pilots of unpressurised aircraft subjected to abnormal pressures?
4. Describe in your own words what causes decompression sickness.
5. Explain, why nitrogen builds up in the body but not carbon dioxide or oxygen?
6. Explain, how this could be avoided by deep-sea divers.

LEVERS

A crowbar is an example of a simple .... which can be used to move heavy ....

It has a .... about which it rotates. When it acts as a force multiplier the .... force needed

is less than the .... force it overcomes. However for this to happen the position of the pivot

is closer to the .... force than it is to the .... force.

A spanner is an example of a lever in action. The .... is the point about which the nut rotates,

the .... force is applied by the pushing hand and the .... force loosens the nut.

We also have levers in our body; the .... eg. arms and legs act as levers. Movement of an arm or leg

is due to the .... of muscles. For example, in the arm, the .... muscle contracts and the

.... muscle relaxes and this enables a .... to be lifted. The elbow is the ....

Muscles which act in this way are called ....

PRESSURE, FORCE AND AREA

The bar graph below shows the pressure exerted by eight objects whose weight is applied over a particular area.
Object A has a weight of 50N which is applied over an area of 10cm².

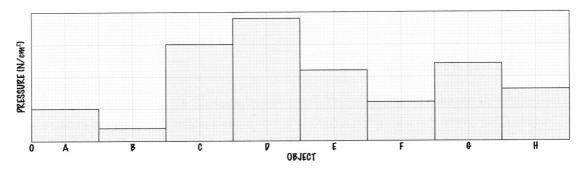

1. Complete the following table. The first one has been done for you.

WEIGHT (N)	AREA (cm²)	OBJECT
50	10	A
110	10	
72		G
	4	D
200		H
	20	B

2. The two objects not included in the table above both apply their weight over an area of 5cm².
   What are their weights?

....

....

Gail and Martin were investigating how the Principle of Moments is affected by the position of the pivot. They were both given 1 metre rulers of uniform thickness. Gail decided to pivot her ruler at the 40cm mark while Martin decided to pivot his ruler at the 50cm mark, the centre of the ruler.

GAIL'S RULER

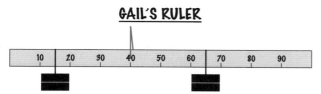

MARTIN'S RULER

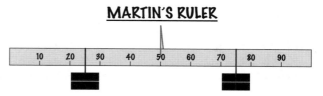

1. Weights were suspended on each side of the pivot and their position altered until the ruler balanced. Their results are given below. Complete each table.

CLOCKWISE			ANTI-CLOCKWISE		
WEIGHT (N)	DISTANCE (cm)	MOMENT (Ncm)	WEIGHT (N)	DISTANCE (cm)	MOMENT (Ncm)
1	20		2	7.5	
2	20		2	18	
3	20		2	27.5	
4	20		2	37	

CLOCKWISE			ANTI-CLOCKWISE		
WEIGHT (N)	DISTANCE (cm)	MOMENT (Ncm)	WEIGHT (N)	DISTANCE (cm)	MOMENT (Ncm)
1	20		2	11	
2	20		2	20	
3	20		2	29	
4	20		2	40	

2. Draw straight line graphs to show their results.

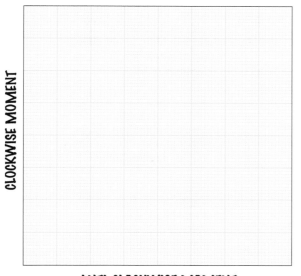

CLOCKWISE MOMENT

ANTI-CLOCKWISE MOMENT

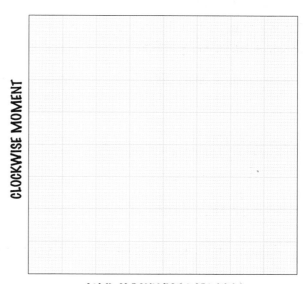

CLOCKWISE MOMENT

ANTI-CLOCKWISE MOMENT

3. What conclusion would Gail come to from her results?

....

....

4. What conclusion would Martin come to from his results?

....

....

5. Explain why their two conclusions are not the same.

....

....